748.2913

Florence, Gene $19.95

Kitchen glassware of the
    Depression years

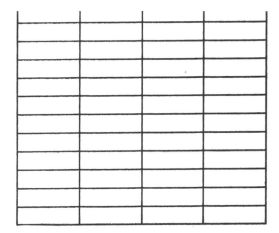

JAN 19 1996

GAYLORD M2

96

Kitchen Glassware

of the Depression Years

Fifth Edition

Gene Florence

COLLECTOR BOOKS
A Division of Schroeder Publishing Co., Inc.

The current values in this book should be used only as a guide. They are not intended to set prices, which vary from one section of the country to another. Auction prices as well as dealer prices vary greatly and are affected by condition as well as demand. Neither the Author nor the Publisher assumes responsibility for any losses that might be incurred as a result of consulting this guide.

SEARCHING FOR A PUBLISHER?

We are always looking for knowledeable people considered to be experts within their fields. If you feel that there is a real need for a book on your collectible subject and have a large comprehensive collection, contact us.

COLLECTOR BOOKS
P.O. Box 3009
Paducah, Kentucky 42002-3009

About The Author

Gene Florence, born in Lexington in 1944, graduated from the University of Kentucky where he held a double major in mathematics and English. He taught nine years in Kentucky at the junior high and high school levels before his glass collecting "hobby" became his full time job.

Mr. Florence has been interested in "collecting" since childhood, beginning with baseball cards and progressing through comic books, coins, bottles, and finally, glassware. He first became interested in Depression Glass after buying an entire set of Sharon dinnerware at a garage sale for $5.00.

He has written several books on glassware: The *Collector's Encyclopedia of Depression Glass*, now in its eleventh edition; *Elegant Glassware of the Depression Era*, now in its sixth edition; *The Collector's Encyclopedia of Akro Agate; The Collector's Encyclopedia of Occupied Japan*, Volumes I, II, III, IV and V; Very Rare Glassware of the Depression Years, (First, Second, Third and Fourth Series) and the *Pocket Guide to Depression Glass*, now in its ninth edition. He recently completed the fifth edition of his innovative Standard Baseball Card Price Guide that has been very well received in card collecting circles.

His 17-year-old Grannie Bear antique shop in Lexington, Ky., has now closed due to the sudden death of his mom, "Grannie Bear," who oversaw that store. Mr. Florence continues to sell glassware, however, via mail order and at Depression Glass shows throughout the country.

If you know of any **unlisted** or **unusual** pieces of kitchen glassware like the examples shown in this book, you may write Mr. Florence at Box 22186, Lexington, KY 40522. If you expect a reply, you must enclose a self-addressed, stamped envelope — and be patient. It is better to write him June through October since writing and researching three or four books each year leaves little time to answer the four to five thousand pieces of correspondence he receives.

Acknowledgments

A space of five years to re-examine the field of kitchenware was admittedly too long a time, but accumulating glassware not already shown in the previous books was a task. The sudden death of "Grannie Bear" prevented me from scheduling a trip to California to photograph some collections there for this book; but it couldn't be helped!

Many people assisted with this book by lending glass for photography on several occasions in the last few years. Pieces accumulated were photographed to add a page or two. Many thanks go to collectors from California to Florida who have offered opinions on pricing, but I have a special debt to Lorrie Kitchen, who not only helped price but spent extra hours searching for items priced that appear in more than one place in the book. All of us have attempted to make this book the finest in its field. Pictures shown herein were taken by photographers Dave Hammell from California, Richard Walker from New York, Kenn Whitmyer from Ohio, and Charley Lynch from Kentucky.

Thanks to the following for lending glass, or pricing information or help in photography: Dan Tucker and Lorrie Kitchen, Terry and Celia McDuffee, Dick and Pat Spencer, Hank and Carla Bowman, Sally Davis, Judy Smith, Stanley and Louise Duda, Sherry Harkins, Carrie Dormitz, Lenore Ewald, Bob and Carole Radcliffe, Edna Barnes, Arland and Marjorie Stokes, Melvin and Linda Sumter, Michelle Rosewitz, Jane White, Sherry Kraus, Lisa Stroup and numerous other collectors who have written me or shared information at shows for the benefit of fellow collectors.

My gratitude must be expressed to the editorial crew of Collector Books, Terri Stalions in particular, for help in putting this book together.

A heartfelt thanks is due the family, Cathy, Marc, Chad, and Becky Florence, and Charles and Sibyl Gaines who have superbly weathered the usual myriad ordeals of travel, shows, book orders and deadlines and the very unusual event of mother's death and the resulting gargantuan task of closing the shop!

Foreword

Availability of kitchenware, or the lack thereof, is the number one concern of collectors. In the five years since I wrote the fourth Kitchen Glassware of the Depression Years, I have been asked over and over, "When is the next book coming out?" Gathering wares for a new book is more like collecting than you think. Choice items for new pictures may be few and far between. We have added an additional 16 pages and eliminated as few photographs as absolutely necessary. I believe it is better to show an item not seen previously than to repeatedly show the same pieces. Please enjoy these 4,900 pieces of kitchenware! It's more than ever shown before, and getting them here was not an easy task! I hope you'll find all the effort taken worthwhile!

As with most collectibles, there are numerous pieces found over and over; but the already hard-to-find items show up less frequently. Exceptional pieces are bought by fervent collectors and until their particular collection is broken up or sold, many rarely found items are not offered again at any price. It takes patience as well as cash to collect. One of the joys of collecting is finding that specific piece that you have been pursuing for a long time. So many collectors have written or stopped by my booth at shows to express to me the joy they have received from collecting glass!

I have observed that more collectors are gathering kitchenware by colors than any other way. Because of this, **colors** are the first listing in this book with **items** and **patterns** following. I'm aware this causes some overlapping of photos and information.

Pricing

All prices in this book are retail prices for **mint condition** glassware. This book is intended to be only a **guide** to prices. A price range has been given for kitchenware items to allow for some wear and a little roughness that is normally not allowed in collecting other forms of Depression Glass. You will note that the price range has been widened in several areas, but particularly in reamer and measuring cup collecting. I have received pricing ideas from several dealers and collectors and the range of pricing was enough to stagger my mind. Since I, ultimately, must take the brunt of pricing discrepancies from collectors and dealers alike, I want you to know that the only rule in pricing seems to be determined by who owns it and who wishes to own it. In other words, only **two** people determine price, the buyer and the seller. **You**, ultimately, have to decide if the price is right for you.

The roughness or usage marks found on Kitchenware is a turn-off to some collectors who search for perfection. Remember, these were **utilitarian** items and were in **use** for years; therefore, most collectors will allow some roughness. This does not mean cracks, chips or chunks are acceptable. To the contrary, these greatly reduce the value of a piece. It simply means that kitchenware collectors are a little more lenient about the condition of the glassware than are collectors of Depression dinnerware. They have to be because **most of the kitchenware does not exist in absolutely mint condition!**

I have seen both higher and lower prices for most items shown; however, the prices listed are prices that collectors somewhere in the country have been willing to pay.

Colors

Any time the word green or pink occurs, it means a transparent (see-through) color. Other color items are described below.

Amethyst – a transparent, violet color.

Black Amethyst – color appears black but will show purple under a strong light.

Blue – "Chalaine," an opaque, sky blue made by McKee; "Cobalt," a transparent, dark blue; "Delphite," an opaque, medium blue made by Jeannette.

Clambroth – translucent off white or translucent green.

Custard – an opaque beige.

Green – "Jad-ite," an opaque green made by Hocking; "Jadite," an opaque green made by Jeannette; "Skokie," an opaque green made by McKee.

White – milk white; milk glass; opal white (all these terms simply indicate a white color); "Vitrock," a white made by Hocking.

Yellow– vaseline, a transparent greenish-yellow; "Seville" yellow, an opaque yellow made by McKee.

Contents

Part 1 – Colors
AMBER (Dark)

This book is divided into three sections: **Color**, **Items**, and **Patterns**, in that order. Thus, some items are pictured more than once. Hopefully, the prices are the same in each case of a repeated item. (I spent days trying to make certain of that.) However, feel free to report any discrepancies you find.

There are hundreds of new things shown in this book with the added pages; but to make room for them, some objects previously shown had to be omitted. I assume that you would prefer to see new items rather than different displays of things seen in earlier editions. However, for anyone discovering Depression era Kitchenware for the first time, we've still included all the basics.

At present, amber is not an avidly sought color, even though many pieces in it are rare. Reamer, measuring cup, and knife collectors are having difficulty finding amber pieces for their collections. Most Fry collectors would love to have the reamer shown in Row 4 or the meat platter in Row 5. By the same standard, various knife collectors are searching for the "Stonex" knife shown in Row 5.

So, keep in mind that not everyone collects Kitchenware by color. Many collectors seek only certain items. Therefore, the competition is intensified between these separate collecting fields.

Row 1:	#1	Embossed "Coffee" canister	85.00– 95.00
	#2	Embossed "Tea" canister	70.00– 75.00
	#3-6	Spice shakers, ea.	20.00– 22.50
	#7	Salt box	150.00–165.00
	#8	Measuring cup	250.00–275.00
Row 2:	#1	Sugar canister	110.00–125.00
	#2	New Martinsville batter set	150.00–175.00
	#3	Cambridge etched grapes design ice bucket	35.00– 40.00
	#4	Valencia reamer, unembossed	250.00–300.00
Row 3:	#1	Water bottle	55.00– 65.00
	#2-5	U.S. Glass mixing bowl set (4)	80.00–100.00
		9" bowl	30.00– 35.00
		8" bowl	20.00– 25.00
		7" bowl	17.50– 22.50
		6" bowl	15.00– 17.50
Row 4:	#1	Cake stand (fairly recent vintage)	15.00– 17.50
	#2	Fry reamer	300.00–325.00
	#3	Butter dish (foreign)	40.00– 50.00
	#4	Butter dish (similar to canisters above)	50.00– 60.00
Row 5:	#1	Indiana Glass reamer	250.00–300.00
	#2	Fry meat platter	50.00– 60.00
	#3	Knife, 8¼", "Stonex"	150.00–175.00
	#4	Knife rest	17.50– 20.00
	#5	Apothecary measure, 1 oz.	25.00– 30.00

AMBER (Continued)

For some reason intense collectors of amber buy the darker shades; however, to have a usable set, you need to observe that amber color tints vary greatly as is portrayed by our pictures. Gathering only one shade of amber would be nearly impossible.

One note regarding the drawer pulls on Row 5. Drawer pulls with small screws are still more in demand than those with large screws ostensibly because smaller screws do not damage furniture as badly. However, you need to know that these are now being reproduced in many different colors. What I have seen are good copies, but the prices have been on a par with the prices of older ones, which is unfortunate.

Row 1:	#1	Chesterfield pitcher	85.00– 90.00
	#2	Chesterfield mug	20.00– 22.50
	#3	Imperial syrup	65.00– 75.00
	#4	Sugar shaker	175.00–200.00
	#5	"Visible" mail box	75.00– 85.00
Row 2:	#1	Cambridge oval covered casserole	30.00– 35.00
	#2	Cambridge covered casserole with underliner	30.00– 35.00
	#3	Cheese dish (possibly foreign)	60.00– 65.00
Row 3:	#1	U.S. Glass 2 cup and reamer top	250.00–300.00
	#2	Cambridge 2-spouted gravy boat	22.50– 25.00
	#3	Cambridge footed cream sauce boat for asparagus platter	20.00– 22.50
	#4	Westmoreland 2-piece reamer	150.00–200.00
	#5	Lemon reamer (foreign)	100.00–110.00
	#6	Oil bottle	25.00– 27.50
Row 4:	#1	Paden City "Party Line" ice bucket	25.00– 27.50
	#2	Same, 14 oz. tumbler	8.00– 10.00
	#3	Paden City egg cup	8.00– 10.00
	#4	Paden City hotel sugar and cover	20.00– 25.00
	#5	Paden City salt box	65.00– 75.00
	#6	Cambridge oil bottle	40.00– 45.00
	#7	Tobacco jar	30.00– 35.00
Row 5:	#1	"Feathered" curtain tie backs, pr.	22.50– 25.00
	#2	"Sandwich" round tie backs, pr.	20.00– 25.00
	#3	"Plume" tie backs or small round, pr.	17.50– 20.00
	#4	et. al. drawer pulls, ea. (large screws)	5.00– 7.00
		Same w/small screws	10.00– 12.50
	#5	Door knobs, set	65.00– 80.00

AMBER and BLACK (Milk glass or amethyst)

The shade of amber most easily found is the lighter shade shown in lower half of the photo on page 11. There is a reluctance on the part of present day collectors to buy amber as a kitchen collectible; and because of this, there have been some price corrections in this book. (That is a polite way of saying some prices have dropped!) Reamers, sugar shakers, and unusual items are still in demand, but common pieces remain difficult to sell. The Cambridge reamer (Row 3, #1) is one of the prime amber collectibles; however, even it is not as easily sold as it was a few years ago! Measuring cups (Row 4, #3 and Row 5, #3) are examples of supply equaling demand.

Black still carries a mystique all its own for collectors. Have you noticed how many modern kitchens are using black as a decorating color? Our home in Florida has a major black color scheme in the kitchen appliances. All five reamers shown on page 13 are prizes worthy of possessing, but they can annihilate the glass budget.

Amber
Page 11

Row	#	Item	Price
Row 1:	#1	Cocktail shaker	75.00– 95.00
	#2-4	Jars (recent vintage)	15.00– 20.00
	#5	Tobacco jar	20.00– 22.50
	#6	Sugar shaker	50.00– 55.00
Row 2:	#1	Batter jug, Paden City	45.00– 50.00
	#2	Tobacco jar	18.00– 20.00
	#3	Sugar shaker, Paden City	160.00–175.00
	#4	Sugar shaker	160.00–175.00
	#5	Sugar shaker	90.00–100.00
	#6	Syrup, Cambridge	40.00– 50.00
Row 3:	#1	Reamer, Cambridge	600.00–700.00
	#2	Reamer, foreign	60.00– 70.00
	#3	Reamer, top only	50.00– 60.00
		Same, complete	150.00–175.00

Row	#	Item	Price
Row 3:		(Continued)	
	#4	Sugar Shaker, Paden City	150.00–175.00
	#5	Syrup	40.00– 45.00
Row 4:	#1	Reamer, Westmoreland	250.00–300.00
	#2	Butter, ¼ lb., Federal	25.00– 30.00
	#3	Measure cup, no handle	35.00– 37.50
	#4	Butter, ¼ lb., Federal	25.00– 30.00
	#5	Jelly jar	12.00– 15.00
Row 5:		**All Federal Glass Company**	
	#1	Butter, 1 lb.	30.00– 35.00
	#2	Butter tub	25.00– 30.00
	#3	Measure cup, w/handle	35.00– 38.00
	#4	Reamer, tab handle	12.50– 15.00
	#5	Reamer, tab handle	275.00–300.00

Black
Page 12

Row	#	Item	Price
Row 1:	#1	Cookie jar, L. E. Smith	75.00– 85.00
	#2	Batter jug, Fenton	125.00– 150.00
	#3	Syrup, same	60.00– 75.00
	#4	Reamer pitcher, Fenton	1,200.00–1,400.00
Row 2:	#1	Ice bucket	50.00– 60.00
	#2	Jar, import?	15.00– 20.00
	#3	Sugar shaker	300.00– 325.00
	#4	Saunders reamer	1,000.00–1,250.00
Row 3:	#1	McKee grapefruit reamer	900.00–1,100.00
	#2	Sunkist reamer	600.00– 700.00
	#3-5	Shakers, ea.	20.00– 25.00
	#6	Tray for batter set	25.00– 30.00

Row	#	Item	Price
Row 4:	#1	Mixing bowl, 9⅜"	40.00– 45.00
		Bowl, 8⅜" (not shown)	35.00– 40.00
		Bowl, 7⅜" (not shown)	32.50– 35.00
		Bowl, 6⅜" (not shown)	25.00– 27.50
		Bowl, 5⅜" (not shown)	20.00– 27.50
	#2	Bowl, 7⅜" McKee	25.00– 30.00
	#3	Mug	22.00– 25.00
	#4	Ladle	20.00– 25.00
Row 5:	#1	McKee, 2 spout	700.00– 800.00
	#2	Reamer, Tricia	1,200.00–1,400.00
	#3	Tray	25.00– 30.00
	#4	Shaker, Fenton hobnail	25.00– 30.00

Page 13

Row	#	Item	Price
Row 1:	#1	Sellers sugar canister	80.00– 90.00
	#2	Salt or pepper, ea.	15.00– 20.00
	#3	McKee batter jug	100.00–110.00
	#4	Cocktail shaker	50.00– 60.00
	#5	Syrup, covered, Fenton	60.00– 80.00
Row 2:	#1	McKee, 4½" salt (harder to find than pepper)	15.00– 20.00
		Same, pepper (weak lettering–50% of prices)	12.00– 15.00
		Same, flour or sugar	20.00– 25.00
	#2	McKee, 3½" sugar (priced as above)	20.00– 25.00
	#3	Covered ice bucket	75.00– 85.00
	#4	McKee tumbler	15.00– 18.00
	#5	Straw in tumbler	4.00– 5.00
	#6	Paden City batter jug set	250.00–275.00

Row	#	Item	Price
Row 3:		All shakers priced as in Row 2 (with those having badly worn or missing lettering 50% of prices listed) EXCEPT last pr.	35.00– 40.00
Row 4:	#1	Butter dish w/crystal top (possibly foreign)	65.00– 75.00
	#2	Egg cup	10.00– 12.50
	#3	Drawer pull, double	12.00– 15.00
	#4	Paden City, "Party Line" napkin holder	115.00–135.00
	#5	Nar-O-Fold Napkin Company Chicago, U.S.A.	115.00–135.00
Row 5:	#1	Punch ladle	75.00– 85.00
	#2-5	Drawer pulls, ea.	10.00– 12.50
	#3	Cambridge salad set	125.00–150.00

BLUE (Chalaine) and PEACOCK BLUE

Chalaine blue is one of the more challenging colors to find in Depression Kitchenware. It is often confused with Delphite blue by beginning collectors. I have always referred to Chalaine as "robin's egg" blue to help distinguish the color from Delphite.

Cathy and I decided to break up the set we were collecting when we moved ... again! Color schemes were vastly different! We made several collectors very happy! Our canisters went to a lady who has since confessed to having a baker's dozen of them!

Several of the costly rolling pins have surfaced lately. Besides the rolling pin, the measuring pitcher without a handle is the most elusive piece. Only two of these have been found and the price is notably high on these. Good strong lettering on the shakers and canisters is necessary; but beware that there are "artists" who have been known to "doctor" this black lettering.

Peacock Blue now seems to be as plentiful as Chalaine, but neither color is abundant. You should find Peacock blue canisters with serious searching. Labeling is not a problem with this color since the names are embossed in the glass.

Chalaine Blue
Page 15

Row 1: #1 Vase, 12"   100.00– 125.00
       #2 Measure pitcher, 4 cup,
             without handle   1,250.00–1,500.00
       #3 Measure pitcher, 4 cup, ftd. 300.00– 400.00
       #4 Pitcher, ftd.
             (possibly Fenton)   200.00– 250.00

Row 2: #1-6 Shakers, ea.   70.00– 75.00
       #7,8 Shakers, embossed   100.00– 125.00
       #9 Measure cup, 2 spout   700.00– 800.00

Row 3: #1 Refrigerator dish, 7¼" sq. 110.00–125.00
       #2 Refrigerator dish, 4" x 5"   40.00– 50.00
       #3 Canister, rnd., 10 oz., blue lid 40.00– 55.00
       #4 Canister, rnd., 24 oz., blue lid 40.00– 55.00
       #5 Canister, rnd., 48 oz., blue lid 65.00– 85.00

Row 4: #1-4 Canisters (press-on lids), ea. 350.00–400.00
       #5 Sunkist reamer   175.00–195.00

Page 16

Row 1: #1 Ladle, screw on handle   175.00– 200.00
       #2 Rolling pin, shaker top 1,500.00–1,800.00
Row 2: #1 Beater bowl, w/spout, 4" tall 60.00– 65.00
       #2,5 Drawer pull, single   10.00– 12.00
       #3 Butter dish, ribbed,
             tab handles   300.00– 325.00
       #4 Fruit jar   75.00– 100.00
       #6 Egg cup   12.00– 15.00

Row 2: (Continued)
       #7 Small jar   17.50– 20.00
Row 3: #1 Mixing bowl, 9¼"   85.00– 95.00
       #2 Same, 7½"   75.00– 85.00
       #3 Same, 6"   65.00– 75.00
       #4 Door knob   75.00– 85.00
Row 4: #1 Mixing bowl, 9"   60.00– 80.00
       #2 Mixing bowl, 9", ribbed   85.00– 95.00
       #3 Flower pot, Akro Agate   15.00– 20.00

Peacock Blue
Page 17

Row 1: #1 Strawholder (probably
             1950's)   200.00–250.00
       #2 L.E. Smith cookie jar   75.00–100.00
       #3 Imperial decanter   30.00– 35.00
       #4 Dispenser (for a liquid
             or syrup)   200.00–250.00
Row 2: #1 Sugar, 5 lb. canister   250.00–275.00
       #2 Coffee, 40 oz. canister   150.00–175.00
       #3 Tea, 20 oz. canister   125.00–150.00
       #4-6 Shakers, 8 oz., ea.   40.00– 50.00
       #7 Salt box   125.00–150.00
Row 3: #1 Ice tub   30.00– 35.00
       #2 Rolling pin   250.00–275.00

Row 3: (Continued)
       #3 Mug   25.00–30.00
Row 4: #1 Jar (paper label, sold
             by route merchants)   15.00–17.50
       #2-8 Tie backs, large pr.   25.00–30.00
             small pr.   20.00–25.00
Row 5: #1, 3 Towel rods, ea.   27.50–30.00
       #2 Double towel rod   35.00–40.00
Row 6: #1, 2 Spoons, ea.   22.50–25.00
       #3, 4 Salad set   55.00–70.00
       #5, 6 Double drawer pulls, ea. 18.00–20.00
       #7-11 Single drawer pulls, ea. 10.00–12.00

SALT PEPPER FLOUR SUGAR FLOUR SUGAR FLOUR SUGAR

CEREAL COFFEE FLOUR TEA

BLUE (Cobalt)

A word of warning to those of you who may have found a cobalt blue rolling pin recently. An "old" cobalt blue rolling pin with a screw-on metal cap was never found. In fact, no rolling pins with screw-on metal lids have ever been found in a transparent color other than crystal. I mention that here because I am receiving letters regularly about these "rare" finds. I'm sorry, but they are all newly made.

The mystique of the cobalt blue color continues. Some collectors recently have been willing to pay "whatever it takes" to finish up their collections. Unfortunately, that makes it difficult to fairly price some rarely found items that have sold recently. Just because a wealthy collector buys an item at a big price does not necessarily mean the next like item on the market will fetch a big price also. Cobalt blue canisters with exceptional lettering and undamaged lids are bringing phenomonal prices. There are a few canisters with worn lettering and chipped lids available, but collectors are willing to pay a premium for mint canisters. Know that lettering is sometimes being redone on worn canisters!

Items with an asterisk (*) in the book have been reproduced! See pages 236-237 for further information. On page 19, Row 2, #1 and #5 have both been reproduced and the price made a downward adjustment for a while. It was only temporary!

Page 19   All Hazel Atlas except last row.

Row 1:	#1-5	Canister w/lid (deduct 75.00-100.00 for worn lettering)	375.00–425.00
Row 2:	#1	2-Cup measure w/reamer top	*250.00–275.00
	#2	Tab-handled orange reamer	250.00–275.00
	#3	Tab-handled lemon reamer	250.00–300.00
	#4	Milk pitcher	85.00–100.00
	#5	1-Cup measure, 3 spout	*350.00–400.00
Row 3:	#1	Stack refrigerator, 4½" x 5", ea.	40.00– 45.00
	#2	Round refrigerator, 5¾"	60.00– 75.00
	#3	Water bottle, 64 oz., 10" tall	55.00– 60.00

Row 3:	(Continued)		
	#4	Hazel Atlas bottle, (possibly medicinal)	20.00– 25.00
	#5	Mixer, Vidrio Products	110.00–125.00
Row 4:	#1	Butter dish	180.00–200.00
	#2	Bowl, 5¾", "Restwell"	17.50– 20.00
	#3	Bowl, 6"	17.50– 20.00
	#4	Tumbler, marked HA	10.00– 15.00
Row 5:	#1	Spoon stirrer	10.00– 12.50
	#2	Curtain tie back	15.00– 17.50
	#3	Drawer pull	10.00– 12.00
	#4, 5	Stirrers, ea.	1.50– 2.50
	#6-8	Spoons or forks, ea.	27.50– 35.00
	#9	Coaster	5.00– 7.50

Page 20

Row 1:	#1	Bowl, 8½" (add $5.00 w/metal)	25.00–30.00
	#2	Bowl, 7⅝" (add $5.00 w/metal)	22.50–27.50
	#3	Bowl, 6⅝" (add $5.00 w/metal)	17.50–22.50
Row 2:	#1	Bowl, 9⅝" (add $5.00 w/metal)	32.50–37.50
	#2	Bowl, 11⅝"	50.00–60.00
	#3	Bowl, 10⅝" (all of above are Hazel Atlas)	75.00–85.00

Row 3:	#1	L.E. Smith water dispenser	350.00–400.00
	#2	Cambridge mug	35.00– 50.00
	#3	Shakers, pr. (possibly bath powder)	18.00– 20.00
Row 4:	#1	L.E. Smith bowl, 8¼"	42.50– 47.50
	#2	Same, 7¼"	37.50– 42.50
	#3	Same, 6¼"	32.50– 37.50
Row 5:	#1	Mustard pot	20.00– 25.00
	#2	Fry cake plate, 3 ftd.	85.00– 95.00
	#3, 4	Fork and spoon, set	50.00– 55.00

Page 21

Row 1:	#1	Barbell cocktail shaker	75.00– 85.00
	#2	Strawholder	250.00–275.00
	#3	Cocktail shaker	40.00– 50.00
	#4	McKee batter jug	80.00– 95.00
Row 2:	#1	New Martinsville batter set	300.00–325.00
	#2, 3	Shakers w/blue tops	35.00– 40.00
	#4	Sugar shaker (older than Depression era)	175.00–200.00
	#5	Sugar shaker	600.00–650.00

Row 2:	(Continued)		
	#6	Tumble up	60.00– 70.00
Row 3:	#1	Paden City batter jug	60.00– 70.00
	#2	Same, milk jug	50.00– 60.00
	#3	Same, syrup jug	50.00– 60.00
	#4	Cambridge reamer	2,000.00–2,500.00
Row 4:	#1	Cobalt rolling pin	400.00– 450.00
	#2	Cobalt handles rolling pin	200.00– 250.00

BLUE (Delphite), Jeannette Glass Co., Late '30's

"Usually a color that is featured on the cover may experience some price escalation. So be forewarned!" With those words I closed my comments on Delphite in the fourth edition. What a prophecy!

After that cover appearance, dealers could not find enough Delphite to satisfy collectors' demands. With a limited amount of pieces being offered for sale, prices on Jeannette's Delphite began to skyrocket and you can see the results in the listings below. Delphite remains one of the most alluring colors of Kitchen collectibles.

Jeannette round canisters are becoming impossible to find at *any* price. The coffee canister remains the easiest of the larger canisters to find, while many collectors have never happened upon the sugar. You may find the smaller round shakers, especially the salt and pepper, but the flour, sugar, and paprika are all elusive. Next to the square shakers in Row 4 is a one-cup measure without a spout. Someone has ground off a badly chipped spout!

The larger-size Delphite reamer is depicted in Row 3, #1 with the more commonly found smaller reamer beside it for comparison. All drippings jars are not found with black lettering. The price without the lettering is only half (or less) of the price shown below. Watch out for repainted letters on these.

I wish you luck in your search for this color.

Row 1:	#1	Canister, 40 oz., sugar	300.00–	350.00
	#2	Same, coffee	300.00–	350.00
	#3	Canister, 20 oz., tea	125.00–	140.00
	#4	Shaker, 8 oz., paprika	100.00–	110.00
	#5	Same, sugar	80.00–	90.00
		Same, flour (not shown)	90.00–	100.00
	#6	Matches holder	75.00–	80.00
	#7	Bowl w/metal beater	60.00–	70.00
Row 2:	#1	Bowl, 5½", horizontal rib	50.00–	60.00
	#2	Measure, 1 cup	45.00–	50.00
		Same, ½ cup	40.00–	45.00
		Same, ⅓ cup	35.00–	40.00
		Same, ¼ cup	30.00–	35.00
	#3	Bowl, 7½", horizontal rib	50.00–	60.00
	#4	Bowl, 9¾", horizontal rib	70.00–	80.00
		Bowl set #1, 3, 4	170.00–	200.00
Row 3:	#1	Reamer, large	1,000.00–	1,250.00
	#2	Reamer, small	65.00–	75.00
	#3, 5	Shaker, salt or pepper	35.00–	40.00
	#4	Drippings jar w/lettering	100.00–	110.00
Row 4:	#1	2-cup pitcher sunflower bottom	60.00–	70.00
	#2	Butter	225.00–	250.00
	#3	Cup measure (spout professionally removed)	25.00–	30.00
	#4, 5	Shaker, square salt or pepper	65.00–	75.00
	#6, 7	Same, flour or sugar	75.00–	85.00
Row 5:	#1-3	Canister, square, 29 oz., 5", ea.	150.00–	175.00
	#4, 5	Mixing bowl set (4) vertical rib	220.00–	260.00
		Bowl, 6", rare	65.00–	75.00
		Bowl, 7"	45.00–	55.00
		Bowl, 8"	45.00–	55.00
		Bowl, 9"	65.00–	75.00

BLUE (Delphite) and BLUE MISCELLANEOUS

The reamer top shown below is atop most Delphite and reamer collectors' want lists. In the center is the only known McKee screw-lid canister. There are surely more somewhere!

As with Jeannette's Delphite, there is not enough McKee Delphite found to satisfy the demand.

Page 24

	#1	Reamer pitcher	1,250.00–1,500.00
	#2	Canister, 48 oz.	150.00– 200.00
	#3	Electric beater	75.00– 85.00

Page 25

Row 1:
	#1	McKee measure pitcher, 4 cup	450.00– 500.00
	#2	McKee measure pitcher, 2 cup	75.00– 85.00
	#3	McKee 48 oz. round canister	100.00– 110.00
	#4	McKee 10 oz. round canister	40.00– 45.00
	#5	Vase	30.00– 35.00
	#6	Ginger (?) jar	15.00– 18.00

Row 2:
	#1	McKee butter dish	225.00– 250.00
	#2	McKee refrigerator dish, 4" x 5"	27.50– 30.00
	#3, 4	Shakers, ea.	75.00– 80.00
	#5	Ash tray, possibly McKee or Pyrex	12.00– 15.00

Row 3:
	#1	Mixing bowl, 9"	65.00– 75.00
	#2	Mixing bowl, 7⅜"	35.00– 40.00
	#3	Bowl w/spout, 4¼"	45.00– 55.00
	#4	Bowl, 4⅜" (cocotte)	12.50– 15.00

Row 4:
	#1	L.E. Smith, 9¼" bowl	60.00– 75.00
	#2	L.E. Smith, 7" bowl	40.00– 50.00
	#3	Fry, cornflower blue reamer	1,500.00–1,750.00
	#4	Hocking, "Block Optic" butter dish	375.00– 425.00

Row 5:
	#1	Cheese dish (possibly foreign)	100.00– 110.00
	#2	Scoop	45.00– 50.00
	#3	Paden City bunny, cotton ball dispenser	65.00– 75.00
	#4	Soap dish, "Home Soap Company"	22.50– 25.00

"CLAMBROTH" WHITE and CRYSTAL

The translucent, washed-out white color shown in the bottom three rows on page 27 is commonly called "Clambroth" (white) by collectors. Although this is a rarely found color (except for the rolling pin), there is not much collector demand for "Clambroth" white either. A remarkable exception to that statement is the oval Pyrex casserole pictured in the middle of Row 3. This casserole is embossed "Pyrex" on one end and "193-197" on the other. Only one of these has appeared so far. You can see additional pieces of "Clambroth" white in the reamer section.

Collectors of crystal kitchenware still have fair prices at their disposal when compared to prices of other popular colored wares. However, be warned that the acquisition of crystal is beginning to deplete even this supply. Many older items can be found at prices comparable to recently manufactured wares.

On page 29, Row 4 #1 is an item marked, "The Pot Watcher." My understanding is that this is placed in the bottom of a pan or pot, and when the pot begins to boil, this glass piece begins to rattle around announcing that the pot is boiling. Another collector wrote that placing this in the bottom would cause the water to not boil over. (These are presently available in hardware stores.)

Page 27

Row 1: #1 Canister, Owens-Illinois,
   frosted, 40 oz. 18.00– 20.00
   #2, 3 Same, 20 oz. 16.00– 18.00
   #4, 5 Cruet, frosted,
   chicken decal, ea. 12.00– 15.00
Row 2: #1 Rolling pin w/wooden
   handles 100.00–125.00
   #2 Sugar shaker, lid w/one hole 40.00– 45.00
   #3, 4 Salt or pepper w/normal lid 15.00– 17.50

Row 3: #1 Canister, large 30.00– 35.00
   #2 Pyrex oval casserole 100.00–125.00
   #3 Canister, medium 25.00– 30.00
   wo/label subtract $5.00 on canisters
Row 4: #1 Tray, 10⅝", square 12.00– 15.00
   #2 Server, 7⅜", round 10.00– 12.00
   #3 Server, 9⅞", round 12.00– 15.00

Page 28

Row 1: #1 Canister, large,
   w/"Taverne" scene 25.00–30.00
   #2 Canister, medium, same
   (rare size) 30.00–35.00
   #3, 4 Shaker, ovoid shape,
   Owens–Illinois, ea. 10.00–12.50
   #5 Canister, ovoid shape,
   Owens-Illinois 20.00–25.00
Row 2: #1 Instant coffee, w/sterling top 25.00–30.00
   #2 "Bohner's Safety crushed fruit
   bowl" (pat. Feb 22, 1898) 20.00–25.00

Row 2: (Continued)
   #3-7 Sneath spice shaker, ea. 10.00–12.50
Row 3: #1 Fleur-de-lis flour canister 20.00–22.50
   #2-4 Canister, 20 oz. ea. 10.00–12.00
   #5 8 oz. Kroger Embassy
   peanut butter 8.00–10.00
   #6 Spee-Dee mixer 20.00–25.00
Row 4: #1-6 Small canister, 16 oz., ea. 7.00– 8.00
   #7 MOXIE (licensed only for
   serving) 20.00–25.00

Page 29

Row 1: #1 Canister, Dutch boy design 15.00–20.00
   #2 Canister, embossed coffee 18.00–20.00
   #3 Canister, emb. coffee,
   Zipper design 20.00–22.00
   #4 "Kwik Whip all purpose mixer" 6.00– 8.00
   #5 "No Drip Server," Federal
   Tool Corp., 1 qt. 10.00–12.00
Row 2: #1 Salt, large 20.00–25.00
   #2 Salt, small 20.00–22.50
   #3 Canister, embossed tea 15.00–18.00
   #4 Syrup, w/glass top (2 pc.) 25.00–30.00
   #5 Pint server (same as #5 in
   Row 1) 6.00– 8.00

Row 3: #1, 6 Glasbake tea kettle, ea. 25.00–30.00
   #2 Canister, raised dots design 15.00–18.00
   #3-5 Shaker, raised dot design, ea. 4.00– 5.00
Row 4: #1 "The Pot Watcher" 8.00–10.00
   #2 McKee Range Tec skillet 9.00–10.00
   #3-8 Six-piece set from box marked
   "Serve U Set" Medco No 86:
   Salt and Pepper, pair 4.00
   Syrup 15.00–17.50
   Ketchup 15.00–17.50
   Marmalade 6.00– 8.00
   Sugar 18.00–20.00

CRYSTAL

Crystal kitchenware lends itself to any kitchen decor and has the added attraction of see-through storage. Prices remain reasonable on most items. Unlike many of today's products that are made to be disposed of after one use, it can be used over and over. The McKee water dispenser shown below has a separate center holder for the ice. I guess that idea never caught on, but it seems like a neat idea to me! The cooler below sells for $85.00–100.00. It is that insert for the ice that can seldom be found.

Row 1:	#1	McKee Glasbake Scientific Measuring Cup	18.00–20.00
	#2-5	Hocking canister w/Dutch decal	15.00–20.00
	#6	Pint measure in tablespoons for coffee, tea & wine	18.00–20.00
Row 2:	#1, 2	John Alden (salt) & Priscilla (pepper), pr.	17.50–20.00
	#3	Westmoreland baby reamer, w/decal	35.00–40.00
	#4	Horseradish jar	10.00–12.50
	#5	Salt box	15.00–17.50
	#6	Toast holder	50.00–65.00
	#7	Spoon holder (Pat. Feb. 11, 1913)	15.00–18.00
Row 3:	#1-8	Dutch shakers (12 oz.), ea. (Cocoa in 6th)	8.00– 9.00
	#9-10	Dutch shakers (16 oz.)	10.00–12.00
Row 4:	#1	Flour canister, 128 oz.	40.00–45.00
	#2	Coffee dripolator	15.00–18.00
	#3	Measure spoon (markings for table, dessert, tea)	4.00– 5.00
	#4	Sprinkler (leaning in back) cardboard wrapped instructions	17.50–20.00
	#5	Cambridge ash tray holder	30.00–35.00
	#6	Jiffy one-cup coffee maker w/filter	8.00–10.00

CUSTARD and "CARAMEL," McKee Glass Company

The darker shade of Custard (shown in the bottom row on page 33), is referred to as "caramel" by collectors. This color may have been experimental or just a bad batch of Custard. Today, we do not have the luxury of obtaining that information. The canister on the far right is not a fired-on color, but a solid, caramel color like the other pieces. I mention that because I have seen a few fired-on pieces similar in color.

There are some avid collectors of the Custard colored ware, but its popularity with most collectors is still lackluster. Many pieces are commonly found, but some are elusive. Although the Sunkist custard reamer is abundant, custard grapefruit reamers are rare.

If you would like a challenge, try putting together a set of four (salt, pepper, flour, sugar) in any particular lettering design. Unless you are lucky enough to buy a complete set at one time, it will take a lot of searching to come up with a matching set.

Page 33

Row 1: #1, 2 Canister, coffee or tea, ea. 35.00– 40.00
        #3 Measure pitcher, 4 cup 30.00– 35.00
        #4 Bowl, 9" 18.00– 20.00

Row 2: #1 Bowl, 8" 15.00– 18.00
        Bowl, 7" (not shown) 12.00– 15.00
        #2 Bowl, 6" 10.00– 12.00
        #3, 4 Shaker, Roman arch, flour, sugar 12.00– 15.00
        #5, 6 Same, salt or pepper 10.00– 12.00

Row 3: #1-4 Salt or pepper shakers, ea. 10.00– 12.00
        #5 Cinnamon shaker 25.00– 30.00
        #6-9 Flour or sugar shaker, ea. 17.50– 20.00

Row 4: #1 Pepper shaker 12.50– 15.00
        #2 Lady w/apron shaker 17.50– 20.00
        #3 Custard or jello 4.00– 5.00
        #4 Pitcher, 2 cup 15.00– 18.00
        #5 Tumbler 8.00– 10.00
        #6 Tom & Jerry mug 12.00– 15.00

Row 5: #1 Reamer, 6" embossed McK 20.00– 25.00
        #2 Grapefruit reamer 600.00–650.00
        #3 Sunkist reamer 25.00– 30.00

Row 6: **All Caramel Color**
        #1 Canister, 40 oz. 65.00– 75.00
        #2 Grapefruit reamer 750.00–850.00
        #3 Sunkist reamer 300.00–350.00
        #4 Measure cup, 2 spout 500.00–600.00
        #5 Canister, 48 oz 85.00–100.00

EMERALD-GLO, FOREST GREEN AND GREEN "CLAMBROTH"

The items pictured on page 35 have been found labeled "Cavalier Emerald-Glo Hand-Made." You will find additional pieces to this set; let me hear what you find! Most pieces are cut with a star. Those with a star cut were made by Paden City. Pieces without a star cut were made by both Paden City and Fenton. Fenton's pieces are a darker green shade when set side by side with those of Paden City. All Emerald-Glo was made for Rubel.

Emerald-Glo
Page 35

Row 1:	#1	Sugar w/liner	18.00–20.00
	#2	Condiment set	25.00–30.00
	#3	Marmalade w/spoon	18.00–20.00
Row 2:	#1	Handled relish	22.50–25.00
	#2	Salad bowl w/fork and spoon	45.00–50.00
	#3	Individual creamer/sugar on tray	20.00–22.50
Row 3:	#1	Covered casserole	25.00–30.00
	#2	Mayonnaise w/spoon	18.00–20.00
	#3	Syrup w/liner	30.00–35.00
Row 4:	#1	Handled server	35.00–40.00
	#2	Handled cheese dish	35.00–40.00

Forest Green
Page 36

Row 1:	#1	Owens-Illinois vinegar or water bottle w/tray	30.00–35.00
		Same w/o tray	12.50–15.00
	#2	Hocking water bottle w/top	25.00–30.00
	#3	Duraglas water bottle	20.00–25.00
	#4	McKee syrup (goes with #5)	30.00–35.00
	#5	Oil & Vinegar set (goes w/#4)	30.00–35.00
Row 2:	#1, 2	Owens-Illinois canisters (ovoid shape), ea.	50.00–55.00
		Same, medium size TEA, RICE (not shown)	30.00–35.00
	#3	Same, shaker size	15.00–17.50
		Prices for #1, 2, 3 (30% to 40% less w/missing lettering)	
	#4	Owens-Illinois embossed COFFEE w/flip top	50.00–65.00
Row 2:	(Continued)		
	#5	Owens-Illinois water bottle	12.50–15.00
Row 3:	#1-3	Owens-Illinois 40 oz. diagonal ridged canister, ea.	22.50–25.00
	#4-5	Same, 20 oz., ea (TEA, RICE)	20.00–22.50
	#6	Same, 10 oz.	8.50–10.00
	#7, 8	Shakers, ea.	3.00–4.00
Row 4:	#1	New Martinsville batter jug	65.00–75.00
	#2	Same, syrup jug	55.00–65.00
	#3	Cruet	35.00–40.00
	#4	Sugar shaker (1950's)	65.00–75.00
Row 5:	#1, 2	Curtain rings, ea.	10.00–12.50
	#3	Rolling pin	125.00–150.00
	#4, 5	Shakers, pr.	17.50–20.00

Green "Clambroth" etc.
Page 37

Row 1:	#1-4	Hocking canisters w/glass lid, 47 oz., ea.	45.00–50.00
	#5-8	Hocking shakers, 8 oz. ea.	17.50–20.00
Row 2:	#1	Hocking oval refrig. dish, 8"	30.00–35.00
	#2	Same, 7"	22.00–25.00
	#3	Same, 6"	15.00–18.00
	#4	Refrigerator jar, 4¼" x 4¾"	25.00–27.50
	#5	Hocking drippings jar (possibly powder jar)	20.00–25.00
	#6	Hocking 2-cup measure	100.00–125.00
Row 3:	#1	Hocking 1-cup measure	150.00–175.00
	#2	Hocking reamer	115.00–125.00
	#3	Fenton reamer top for pitcher	45.00–50.00
	#4	Jadite Sunkist (there is one that is much more translucent than this)	20.00–25.00
Row 3:	(Continued)		
	#5	Cold cream jar	15.00–17.50
	#6	Mug	30.00–35.00
Row 4:	#1	Owl "tumble-up" nite set (pitcher & glass as top)	85.00–100.00
	#2	Butter dish	65.00–75.00
	#3	McKee Hall's refrigerator dish, 4" x 6"	14.00–16.00
	#4	Water dispenser w/crystal top	55.00–65.00
Row 5:	#1	Ice bucket, Fenton	50.00–55.00
	#2	Whipped cream pail	35.00–40.00
	#3	Fenton pitcher missing lid (as pictured)	75.00–85.00
	#4	Towel bar holders, pr.	20.00–25.00
	#5	Sugar shaker	30.00–35.00
	#6	"Serv-All" napkin holder	150.00–175.00

GREEN "CLAMBROTH" and JADITE

As with "Clambroth" white, the term "Clambroth" refers to a collector name for the translucent green pictured on pages 37 and 39. It is not a company name. Shown on pages 40 and 41 are a combination of different companies' Jadite. Hocking spelled their color Jad-ite. The only spouted Jadite measuring cup that I have heard about is shown at the top of page 40. On page 41 in Row 3 is a Jad-ite skillet with a label reading, "Yours with Gold Medal Flour; 1 w 25 lb. sack; 2 w 50 lb. sack; New Fire-King Oven Ware."

Page 39

Row 1:	#1	Pitcher (Fenton?)	50.00– 60.00
	#2	Tumbler to match above	8.00– 10.00
	#3	Fenton ice bucket & lid	100.00–110.00
	#4	Tumbler, ftd.	12.00– 15.00
	#5	Sherbet	7.50– 9.00
	#6	Door knob set	65.00– 75.00
Row 2:	#1	Mixing bowl, 8¾"	20.00– 25.00
	#2	Same, 7¾"	15.00– 20.00
	#3	Same, 6¾"	12.00– 15.00
	#4	Powder shaker?	20.00– 22.50
Row 3:	#1	Ashtray	5.00– 6.00
	#2	Wall tumbler holder	10.00– 12.50
	#3	Coaster	8.00– 10.00
	#4	Furniture "foot rest" (per 1920's Montgomery Ward catalogue)	4.00– 5.00
	#5	Jadite towel bar in rear	25.00– 30.00

Row 3:		(Continued)	
	#6	Soap dish	15.00– 17.50
	#7	Jade ashtray	5.00– 8.00
	#8	Jade makeup holder	15.00– 18.00
Row 4:	#1, 2	Canisters, fired-on ea.	25.00– 30.00
	#3	Decanter, pinched	100.00–125.00
	#4	Water bottle	100.00–125.00
	#5	Bowl, 4¾" twist design	10.00– 12.00
	#6	McKee bottoms up w/coaster (coaster $90.00-100.00)	130.00–145.00
Row 5:	#1	Jadite vinegar cruet	150.00–175.00
	#2	Refrigerator dish, wedge shaped	15.00– 20.00
	#3	Refrigerator w/jade lid	8.00– 10.00
	#4	Cigarette ashtray	15.00– 17.50
	#5	Bowl, 4½"	10.00– 12.00

Page 40

Row 1:	#1	Spouted ½ cup measure	75.00– 85.00
	#2	Jeannette souvenir shakers, pr.	100.00–125.00
Row 2:	#1	Fire-King miniature skillet	35.00– 40.00

	#2-5	Child's size 3" canister, ea. (don't confuse w/reg. 3" spice shakers, p. 43)	125.00–150.00
Row 3:	#1-4	Jeannette toiletry shakers, ea.	90.00–110.00

Page 41

Row 1:	#1	Hocking Jad-ite 7½" bowl (decorated)	12.50–15.00
	#2	McKee embossed Salt	40.00–45.00
	#3	McKee 4" x 5" drippings	75.00–85.00
	#4	Jeannette Epsom Salt	65.00–75.00
	#5	Hocking Jad-ite 6½" bowl (decorated)	10.00–12.00
Row 2:	#1	Hocking embossed Fire-King mug	20.00–25.00
	#2	Hocking 7 oz. mug	5.00– 6.00
	#3	Hocking 16 oz. pitcher	15.00–20.00
	#4	Hocking St. Denis cup	6.00– 8.00
	#5	Hocking 6 oz. straight cup	5.00– 6.00
Row 3:	#1	"Swedish Modern," "Jad-ite," 11" mixing bowl, 3 qt.	18.00–20.00

		Same, 9½", 2 qt. (not shown)	16.00–18.00
		Same, 8", 1 qt. (not shown)	12.50–15.00
	#2	Same, 6½", 1 pt.	10.00–12.00
	#3	Jad-ite ¼ pound butter	20.00–25.00
	#4	Jad-ite one spout skillet	20.00–25.00
		Same w/label	25.00–30.00
Row 4:	#1	Leftover refrigerator jar	10.00–12.00
	#2,3	Plate, 9⅝", 5 compartment	12.50–15.00
		Cup, 6 oz.	5.00– 6.00
	#4	Handiwhip w/beater	20.00–25.00
Row 5:	#1	Jad-ite Mixing bowl, 9"	12.00–14.00
	#2	Same, 8"	10.00–12.00
	#3	Same, 7"	8.00–10.00
	#4	Same, 6"	7.00– 9.00

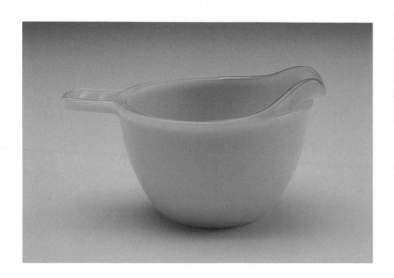

GREEN JADITE, Jeannette and McKee Companies,
(Called "SKOKIE GREEN" by McKee)

Jadite continues to be very popular with collectors. Although there are some price discrepancies between dark and light colors of Jadite, there are still more collectors buying the lighter color. The price of many of the abundantly produced items remains equitable despite heavy demand. Other items, as can be seen by the price, are not so easily found. The batter jug shown in the bottom row can be found. It is the lid that is nigh impossible!

Page 43 (Jeannette Glass Co.)

Row 1:	#1-4	Canister, square, 5½" high, 48 oz., ea.	40.00–45.00
		Same, Floral pattern inside lid	40.00–45.00
	#5	Beater bowl, w/beater	25.00–30.00
Row 2:	#1, 2	Jadite, light, salt or pepper	15.00–17.50
	#3, 4	Same, flour or sugar	20.00–22.50
	#5, 6	Jadite, dark, salt or pepper	15.00–17.50
	#7, 8	Same, flour or sugar	20.00–22.50
	#9	Butter, light	35.00–40.00
Row 3:	#1	Reamer, large, light	20.00–22.00
	#2	Same, dark	22.00–25.00
	#3	Refrigerator dish, 5" x 5" (Floral lid)	20.00–22.00
	#4	Butter, dark	40.00–45.00
Row 4:	#1-4	Canister, square, 29 oz., ea.	35.00–40.00

Row 4:	(Continued)		
	#5	Refrigerator dish, 10" x 5", (Floral lid)	35.00–40.00
Row 5:	#1-4	Spice canister, 3", ea.	45.00– 55.00
	#5	Child's size cannister "sugar" (others include coffee, cereal, tea)	125.00–150.00
	#6	Refrigerator dish, 4" x 4"	11.00– 13.00
	#7	Same, 4" x 8"	18.00– 20.00
Row 6:	#1	Batter jug (bottom only - $50.00)	200.00–250.00
	#2	Salt box	175.00–195.00
	#3	Reamer pitcher, 2 cup, light	20.00– 22.50
	#4	Same, dark (price varies as top & bottom match correctly)	60.00– 75.00

Page 44 (Jeannette Glass Co.)

Row 1:	#1, 2	Canister, round, screw-on lid, 40 oz. coffee, light or dark	60.00– 70.00
	#3	Same, sugar	65.00– 75.00
	#4, 5	Same, 16 oz., tea	40.00– 45.00
	#6	Vase	12.00– 15.00
Row 2:	#1, 3	Salt or pepper	10.00– 12.00
	#2	Drippings (no lettering - $20.00)	40.00– 45.00
	#4, 5	Flour or sugar	12.00– 15.00
	#6, 7	Decorated salt or pepper	12.00– 15.00
	#8-10	Bicarbonate soda or mouth wash	90.00–110.00
Row 3:	#1	Round crock, 40 oz., knob	40.00– 45.00
	#2	Tumbler, 12 oz.	12.00– 15.00
	#3	Sugar shaker, dark	60.00– 65.00
	#4	Sugar shaker, light	55.00– 60.00

Row 3:	(Continued)		
	#5	Round refrigerator dish, 32 oz.	22.00–25.00
Row 4:	#1	Bowl, 5½", horizontal rib	12.00–15.00
	#2	Bowl, 8", vertical rib	15.00–17.50
	#3	Same, 7"	12.00–15.00
	#4	Same, 6"	10.00–12.00
		Same, 9" (not shown)	18.00–20.00
Row 5:	#1	Match holder (lettering $30.00–35.00)	10.00–12.00
	#2	Ashtray	6.00– 8.00
	#3	Reamer, small, light	20.00–22.00
	#4	Same, dark	22.00–25.00
Row 6:	#1	Bowl, 9¾", horizontal rib	30.00–35.00
	#2	Same, 7½"	23.00–25.00
	#3	Bowl, 9¾", vertical rib	20.00–22.00

Page 45 (McKee Glass Co.)

Row 1:	#1-4	Canister, 48 oz., screw-on lid, ea.	50.00– 55.00
	#5	Bottoms down mug	125.00–135.00
	#6	Pitcher, 4 cup	25.00– 30.00
Row 2:	#1	Reamer, large	22.00– 25.00
	#2	Reamer, small	20.00– 22.00
	#3	Refrigerator dish, 4" x 5"	12.00– 15.00
	#4	Pitcher, 2 cup	15.00– 20.00
Row 3:	#1	Bowl, 9"	15.00– 18.00
		Same, 8" (not shown)	12.00– 15.00
		Same, 7" (not shown)	10.00– 12.00
		Same, 6" (not shown)	8.00– 10.00
	#2	Marked 'McK' pat. pend. (any ideas?)	10.00– 12.00
	#3	"Roman" arch side panel, salt	22.50– 25.00
	#5, 7	Same, cinnamon or spice	35.00– 38.00
	#4, 6, 8	Same, pepper, flour or sugar	20.00– 25.00

Row 3:	(Continued)		
	#9	Tumbler or egg cup	8.00– 12.00
Row 4:	#1	"Tom & Jerry" bowl	65.00– 75.00
	#2	Measure cup, 2 spout	160.00–175.00
	#3	Baker, 5" x 3½", oval	10.00– 12.00
	#4	Grapefruit reamer	135.00–150.00
Row 5:	#1	"Tom & Jerry" mug	12.00– 15.00
	#2	Same, cup	12.00– 15.00
	#3	Egg beater bowl, w/spout	15.00– 17.50
	#4	Canister, round, 10 oz.	13.00– 15.00
		Same, 24 oz. (not shown)	18.00– 20.00
		Same, 40 oz. (not shown)	22.50– 25.00
	#5	Baker, 5" x 7", oval	12.00– 15.00
	#6	Custard cup	5.00– 6.00
Row 6:	#1	Measure pitcher, 4 cup, (sans handle)	300.00–350.00
	#2-5	Canister, 28 oz., square, ea.	40.00– 45.00
	#6	Saunders reamer	1,200.00–1,400.00

GREEN TRANSPARENT ASSORTED ITEMS

The box of scoops shown below has been found in both crystal and green. I had purchased one green scoop of each size a few years ago; recently, a set in the original wooden enclosure was found. The individual scoops were already photographed for page 47, but I thought you might wish to see the whole set. The crystal set was found in an old hardware store with screws, nuts, and bolts residing therein. I suspect these were more practical for seeds, but going by the hunks of glass missing — maybe not. Notice the tissue holder on the second row of page 47, another unusual find.

Page 46

Row 1:	#1	Small scoop	30.00– 35.00
	#2	Large scoop	35.00– 40.00
	#3	Set as pictured in box	500.00–600.00

Page 47

Row 1:	#1	Cambridge oil and vinegar	75.00– 85.00
	#2	Paden City parfait	10.00– 12.00
	#3	Ice bucket w/metal drainer	30.00– 35.00
	#4	Georgian ice bucket	35.00– 40.00
Row 2:	#1	Tissue holder	250.00–300.00
	#2	Moisture proof salt shaker	35.00– 40.00
	#3	Small scoop	30.00– 35.00
	#4	Large scoop	35.00– 40.00
Row 3:	#1	Owens-Illinois shaker	7.50– 8.00
	#2	Tie back w/screw	10.00– 12.50
	#3-5	Assorted knobs, ea.	8.00– 10.00
	#6,7	Spoon and fork, set	40.00– 45.00
	#8	"Holt Soap Saver"; Duro Hock Co.; Chicago	15.00– 20.00

Row 3:	(Continued)		
	#9	Shaker	4.00– 5.00
Row 4:	#1	Mixing bowl, 6½"	10.00– 12.00
	#2	Same, 5¾"	8.00– 10.00
	#3	"Tea Room" banana split	80.00– 90.00
	#4	Refrigerator dish ("To seal, turn cover to drop to slots")	22.50– 25.00
Row 5:	#1	Mixing bowl, 9½"	25.00– 30.00
	#2,3	Heisey frosted spoon and fork	85.00–100.00
	#4	Pyrex casserole	12.00– 14.00
	#5,6	Cambridge spoon and fork set	100.00–110.00
	#7	U.S. Glass slick handle bowl w/cover	30.00– 35.00

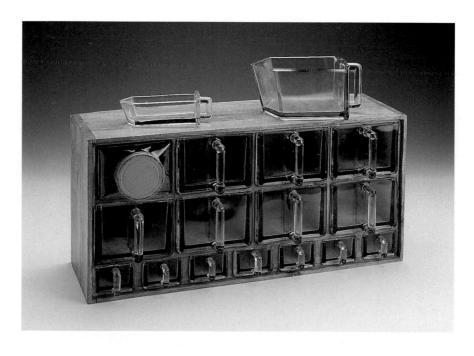

GREEN TRANSPARENT, Jeannette, Hazel Atlas, Federal, and Others

Notice Fenton's "Ming" patterned reamer on page 50, Row 3, #4 that is not shown in the reamer section of the book. That coffee wall dispenser shown in the bottom row of page 51 is giving headaches to several trying to get one. Both items are luring collectors.

Page 49   All Jeannette Glass Co.

Row 1: #1 "Hex Optic" reamer
bucket 35.00– 40.00
#2 Beater bowl 20.00– 25.00
#3 Cruet, w/correct stopper 85.00– 90.00
#4 Jenkins batter jug 125.00–135.00
Row 2: #1 "Hex Optic" sugar
shaker 165.00–175.00
#2 Sugar shaker 50.00– 60.00
#3 Sugar shaker 50.00– 60.00
#4 Mug 25.00– 27.50
#5 Measure cup, tab handle 25.00– 28.00
#6 2-cup measure (Sunflower
bottom) 75.00– 85.00
Row 3: #1 "Hex Optic" 4½" x 5"
'frige' jar 18.00– 22.00

Row 3: (Continued)
#2 Same, dark 18.00– 22.00
#3 Same, butter 65.00– 75.00
#4 "Floral," 5" x 5" 55.00– 65.00
Row 4: #1 Reamer, large 20.00– 22.00
#2 Tab reamer 12.50– 15.00
#3 Reamer top (fits pitcher
or bucket) 10.00– 12.00
#4 Butter 35.00– 40.00
Row 5: #1 Covered 9" bowl 35.00– 40.00
#2 Salt box, 6", "SALT"
on lid 165.00–175.00
#3 Butter, 2-lb. box 125.00–150.00

Page 50

Row 1: #1 Paden City "Party Line"
crushed fruit/cookie jar 65.00– 70.00
#2-4 Cambridge set etched
#732 200.00–250.00
Row 2: #1 Stack sugar/creamer/plate 50.00– 60.00
#2, 3 Marmalade, ea. 20.00– 25.00
#4 Stack set: Westmoreland sugar
creamer/plate/shakers 60.00– 70.00
#5, 6 Curtain tie back, ea. 8.00– 10.00
#7 Ash tray 8.00– 10.00
Row 3: #1 Cambridge gravy &
underliner 65.00– 75.00
#2 Bowl, 7¾" 10.00– 12.50
#3 Toothbrush holder,
frosted 12.50– 15.00

Row 3: (Continued)
#4 Fenton "Ming" reamer 500.00–600.00
#5 Measure cup, 20 oz. 125.00–150.00
Row 4: #1 Bottom to jar or canister 18.00– 20.00
#2 Kompakt dish units, 8" x 4"
(Pat. June 16, 1925) 55.00– 65.00
#3 Towel bar 30.00– 35.00
#4, 5 Curtain tie backs, pr. 18.00– 20.00
#6-8 Drawer pulls, ea. (large
backs $6.00–8.00); small
backs 7.00– 8.00
#9 Double drawer pull 18.00– 20.00

Page 51

Row 1: #1 "Busy Betty" washing
machine 250.00–300.00
#2 Barrel cookie jar 50.00– 60.00
#3 4-cup measure pitcher 600.00–650.00
#4 Single doorknob 30.00– 35.00
#5 Canister embossed
COFFEE 110.00–120.00
Row 2: #1 Rolling pin 400.00–450.00
#2 "Zipper" canister em-
bossed TEA 85.00–100.00

Row 3: #1 Child's washboard embossed CRYSTAL 150.00–200.00
#2 Double towel bar 35.00– 40.00
#3 Double doorknob 100.00–110.00
Row 4: #1, 5 Store shelf supports, ea. 25.00– 35.00
#2 Pickle jar 85.00–100.00
#3 Door hook (screw-in
type) 20.00– 22.00
#4 Wall coffee dispenser 350.00–400.00

GREEN TRANSPARENT, U.S. Glass, Tufglass, and Others

If anyone did know the purpose of the piece marked "ORASORB" (Row 1, #6), they didn't write. Everyone would like to know. Be wary of the embossed "salt or pepper" shown in Row 2. They have been reproduced in several colors including cobalt blue that was never made originally. The embossed "flour or sugar" have not been reproduced.

Page 53

Row 1: #1 Canister, Hazel Atlas 40.00– 45.00
#2 Canister, McKee (RARE) 55.00– 65.00
#3, 4 Syrup, Hazel Atlas, ea. 25.00– 30.00
#5 Syrup, Paden City 30.00– 35.00
#6 "Orasorb" container 75.00– 80.00
Row 2: #1, 2 Shaker, embossed salt or pepper *30.00– 35.00
#3, 4 Same, embossed flour or sugar 65.00– 75.00
#5 FAN FOLD napkin holder 100.00–120.00
#6 Measure cup, 3 spout, Federal 32.50– 35.00
#7 Hazel Atlas tumbler 8.00– 10.00
#8 Measure cup, Paden City 100.00–125.00
Row 3: #1 Mixing bowl, 9" 18.00– 20.00

Row 3: (Continued)
Same, 8" (not shown) 15.00– 17.50
#2 Same, 7" 12.00–14.00
#3 Same, 6" 10.00–12.00
#4 Same, 5" 7.50–10.00
Row 4: #1 Butter, Hazel Atlas 35.00–40.00
#2 Cheese plate ? 15.00–20.00
#3 Measure cup (slightly oval) 40.00–50.00
#4 Reamer top (scalloped edges) 45.00–50.00
Row 5: #1 Fry tray 'Not heat resisting glass' 70.00–80.00
#2 Lattice design refrigerator jar 15.00–18.00
#3 Warming dish, two inserts 65.00–75.00

Page 54

Row 1: #1 Sanitary jar 135.00–150.00
#2 U.S. Glass reamer pitcher (snowflake in bottom) 50.00– 65.00
#3 Slick-handled 9" covered bowl 35.00– 40.00
w/o lid 15.00– 20.00
Row 2: #1 Fluted sundae 15.00– 18.00
#2 Soda 10.00– 12.00
#3 Canning funnel 35.00– 40.00
#4 Cruet 25.00– 30.00
#5 Batter syrup (see page 81 Row 3 #2) 35.00– 45.00
#6 U.S. Glass, 5" x 5" 15.00– 18.00

Row 3: #1 Flask (hard day in kitchen!) 35.00– 45.00
#2 "Tea Room" banana split 80.00– 90.00
#3 Fluted sundae 20.00– 22.50
#4 Cup, slick handle 8.00– 10.00
#5 Banana split 20.00– 25.00
Row 4: #1,3 Flat banana split, ea. 22.00– 27.00
#2 9-oz. tumbler 8.00– 10.00
#4 U.S. Glass covered dish 15.00– 20.00
Row 5: #1,2 Salad set 75.00– 85.00
#3 Spoon holder 175.00–200.00
#4 Mug 20.00– 25.00

**Tufglas
Page 55**

Row 1: #1 J.E. Marsden Glassworks mixing bowl, 5 pt., 10" 40.00– 45.00
#2 Same, 3 pt., 9", made in Ambler, Pa. 35.00– 40.00
#3 Same, 2 pt., 8", also not for oven use 30.00– 35.00
#4 Same, 1½ pt., 7", for mixing, cooling & storing food 25.00– 30.00
Row 2: #1 Butter dish 65.00– 70.00
#2 Refrigerator dish, 3" x 6" 20.00– 25.00
#3 Refrigerator dish, 6½" sq. 30.00– 35.00
#4 "Tufglas Refrigerator Hydrator" No. 1 65.00– 70.00
Row 3: #1 Tufglas tab-handled spouted bowl 30.00– 35.00
#2 One-handled "No Splash Mixer" 35.00– 40.00
#3 Measure pitcher, 36 oz. 125.00–140.00
#4 Funnel 85.00– 95.00

Row 3: (Continued)
#5 Custard, "Trade Mark Tufglas Registered" 8.00– 10.00
Row 4: #1 Reamer 75.00–85.00
#2 Bowl, round, 4" 8.00–10.00
#3 "Kold or Hot" small covered casserole 12.00–15.00
#4 Jello mold 15.00–17.50
#5 "Kold or Hot" Sanitary Food Mold 18.00–20.00
Row 5: #1 4-cup "Kold or Hot" measure pitcher 55.00–65.00
#2 Round refrigerator dish, "To seal, turn cover" 30.00–35.00
#3 "Sanitary Butter Box," top only 30.00–35.00
#4 Round bowl, wrinkled ridge, "Kold or Hot" 12.00–15.00
#5 Custard w/ridges, "Kold or Hot" 2.00– 3.00

*See pages 236 – 237

53

GREEN TRANSPARENT MISCELLANEOUS

Possibly the most coveted green canister set collectors are searching for is the Sneath set shown in Row 2, page 57. Very few sets have been completed over the years. The "Zipper" set shown in Row 3 is also very desirable, and can be found with less difficulty.

On page 58 in the bottom row is a Jenkins reamer pitcher set. It takes all three pieces to fetch the listed price.

Page 57

Row 1:	#1	Strawholder, tall	400.00–450.00
	#2	Strawholder, fancy base	400.00–450.00
	#3	Strawholder, short	350.00–375.00
	#4	Paden City, 'Rena' line tumbler	8.00– 10.00
	#5	Same, pitcher	35.00– 40.00
Row 2:	#1	Paden City syrup w/liner	45.00– 50.00
	#2	Bullet-shaped sugar shaker w/dots on top made by McKee	150.00–160.00
	#3-9	Sneath spice shakers, ea	40.00– 50.00
	#10	Sneath embossed TEA	175.00–200.00
	#11	Same, embossed COFFEE	250.00–275.00

Row 3:	#1	"Zipper" large canister	200.00–225.00
	#2	Same, embossed COFFEE	175.00–200.00
	#3	Same, embossed TEA	115.00–125.00
	#4-6	Same, spice shakers	35.00– 40.00
	#7	Holt soapsaver dish	20.00– 25.00
Row 4:	#1	Batter jug Paden City w/lid	65.00– 75.00
	#2	Paden City "Party Line" napkin holder	100.00–125.00
	#3	Pitcher	35.00– 45.00
	#4	Jenkins pitcher	40.00– 45.00

Page 58

Row 1:	#1	Canister, sugar	100.00–125.00
	#2	Cocktail shaker	18.00– 20.00
	#3	Ring cocktail shaker	20.00– 22.50
	#4	Apothecary jar	30.00– 35.00
	#5	Cookie, frosted	40.00– 45.00
Row 2:	#1	Spouted mixing bowl	20.00– 22.50
	#2	Butter tub	25.00– 30.00
	#3-5	Three jar set	60.00– 70.00
		w/black tray (not shown)	100.00– 115.00
	#6	Mustard	15.00– 17.50
	#7	Spouted bowl, 4½"	15.00– 20.00

Row 3:	#1	Canister, similar to first item in Row 1	30.00– 35.00
	#2	Punch ladle	40.00– 45.00
	#3	Cambridge fork	40.00– 45.00
	#4	Knife rest	15.00– 17.50
Row 4:	#1	Jenkins reamer pitcher w/lid shown beside it	500.00–550.00
	#3	Canister embossed TEA	80.00– 85.00
	#4	Salt	85.00–100.00
	#5	Large salt	125.00–135.00

Page 59

Row 1:	#1	Churn	250.00–285.00
	#2	L.E. Smith cookie	100.00–110.00
	#3	Imperial cocktail shaker	30.00– 35.00
	#4	Cocktail shaker (Sweet Ad-Aline painted on side)	25.00– 30.00
Row 2:	#1	Reamer, called "Speakeasy" by collectors	35.00– 40.00
	#2	Hocking pinched-in decanter	35.00– 45.00
	#3	Cookie jar	35.00– 40.00
	#4	Jar	30.00– 35.00
	#5	Paden City ftd. tumbler	10.00– 12.00

Row 2:	(Continued)		
	#6	Glass straw	4.00– 5.00
Row 3:	#1	Paden City sundae	18.00–20.00
	#2	Covered round dish, 7¼"	27.50–30.00
	#3	Same, 8¼"	32.50–35.00
	#4	Crock, 6¼"	37.50–40.00
Row 4:	#1	Tufglas refrigerator dish, 5⅞" sq.	20.00–25.00
	#2	Cold cream jar	8.00–10.00
	#3	Twisted towel bar	20.00–25.00
	#4	Coffee pot lid	5.00– 6.00
	#5	Drawer pull	5.00– 7.00

GREEN TRANSPARENT, Hocking Glass Company

The once plentiful supply of Hocking green is a thing of the past. New collectors are finding that many pieces are not to be found. The "Vegetable Freshener" (embossed on top) that is shown in Row 3 on page 63 is missing from many collections.

That water bottle in Row 1, #3, page 61 is more abundant than previously thought. Price has remained steady.

Page 61

Row 1:	#1	Decanter, pinched in	40.00– 45.00
	#2	Water bottle	22.00– 25.00
	#3	Water bottle	30.00– 35.00
	#4	Water bottle	20.00– 22.00
	#5	Decanter (same stopper as Cameo)	35.00– 40.00
Row 2:	#1-6	Pretzel Set (pitcher, jar, 4 mugs)	280.00–315.00
		Pitcher, 60 oz.	20.00– 22.00
		Pitcher, 80 oz. (not shown)	20.00– 25.00
		Mug, ea.	30.00– 32.50
		Pretzel jar	80.00– 95.00
Row 3:	#1, 2	Water bottles, 32 oz., 2 styles	22.00– 25.00
	#3	Same, 62 oz.	22.00– 25.00
	#4, 5	Water bottles, raised panels, 32 oz	22.00– 25.00
		Same, 62 oz.	22.00– 25.00

Page 62

Row 1:	#1-3	Paneled mixing bowl, 11½"	22.00–25.00
		10¼"	18.00–20.00
		9½"	15.00–17.50
Row 2:	#1, 3, 4	8½"	12.00–15.00
		7½"	10.00–12.00
		6¾"	12.00–15.00
	#2	8½" bowl, embossed Diamond Crystal Salt	18.00–20.00
Row 3:	#1-4	Mixing bowl, 9½"	12.00–15.00
		8¾"	10.00–12.50
		7¾"	10.00–12.50
		6¾"	8.00–10.00
Row 4:	#1	Mixing bowl, 10½"	15.00–18.00
	#2	Batter bowl, handled	20.00–25.00
	#3	Batter bowl	25.00–28.00

Page 63

Row 1:	#1	Butter dish	25.00– 30.00
	#2	Block Optic butter dish	40.00– 45.00
	#3	Refrigerator dish, Block design, 4¼" x 4¾"	20.00– 25.00
Row 2:	#1-3	Panelled refrigerator dish, 8" x 8"	25.00– 30.00
		Same, 4" x 8"	18.00– 20.00
		Same, 4" x 4"	15.00– 17.50
Row 3:	#1	"Vegetable Freshener" embossed on top	125.00–140.00
	#2, 3	Indent handle, 4" x 4", refrigerator dish	18.00– 20.00
		Same, 4" x 8"	22.00– 25.00
Row 4:	#1-4	Oval rcfrigerator jars (2 style knobs), 8"	27.50– 30.00
		Same, 7"	25.00– 27.50
		Same, 6"	20.00– 22.50
Row 5:	#1	Crock, 8"	40.00– 45.00
		Crock, 6½" (not shown)	30.00– 32.50
	#2	Crock, 5"	25.00– 27.50
	#3, 4	Round refrigerator jar and cover, 9"	25.00– 30.00
		Same, 7" (not shown)	22.00– 25.00
		Same, 5"	18.00– 20.00

GREEN TRANSPARENT and FIRED-ON COLORS,
Hocking and Others

Hocking canisters are the most popular of all those shown in this book, ostensibly because they can be found and the price is well within the range of most collectors. Finding canisters with perfect glass lids is a difficult task; the screw-type metal lid style is harder to find, but less in demand. In Florida, I prefer the screw-type because they are somewhat more moisture proof.

There is a 4-oz. provision jar to go with the other four in Row 3, page 65. I suspect that it is rare because it was never shown in Hocking's catalogues.

To save my answering letters, note that newly made labels for Hocking or Owens-Illinois canisters can be ordered from: Lorrie Kitchen, 3905F Torrance, Toledo, OH 43612. Write for price and styles if your labels are missing.

There are beginning to be more collectors for the fired-on colors. You will find additional photos of fired-on colors on pages 77 and 79.

Page 65

Row 1:	#1-5 Canisters, 47 oz. w/glass lid	40.00–45.00	
	#6-8 Shakers, ea.	10.00–12.00	
Row 2:	#1 Canister, screw-on lid, 64 oz.	40.00–45.00	
	#2, 3 Same, 40 oz.	40.00–45.00	
	#4 Same, 20 oz.	40.00–45.00	
	#5 Shaker, 8 oz., labeled "Domino Sugar"	12.00–15.00	
	#6, 7 Shakers, ea.	10.00–12.00	
Row 3:	#1-4 Provision jars, 64 oz.	30.00–35.00	
	Same, 32 oz.	22.50–25.00	
	Same, 16 oz.	14.00–16.00	

Row 3:	(Continued)		
	Same, 8 oz.	12.00–15.00	
	Same, 4 oz. (not shown)	40.00–50.00	
	#5, 7 Round shakers, pr.	40.00–50.00	
	#6 Drip jar	35.00–40.00	
Row 4:	#1 Canister	25.00–30.00	
	#2-5 Smooth sided canister, 40 oz., screw-on lid	25.00–30.00	
	Same, 20 oz.	20.00–25.00	
	Same, 8 oz., ea.	10.00–12.00	
	#6, 7 Shakers (sold individually as sugar shakers), ea.	25.00–30.00	
	#8, 9 Milk bottle caps, ea.	4.00– 5.00	

Page 66

Row 1:	#1 Cocktail shaker	20.00–22.50	
	#2 Cocktail shaker (pinched-in sides)	25.00–30.00	
	#3 Onion chopper	15.00–17.50	
	#4 Cigarette jar, ash tray on top	14.00–16.00	
	#5 Toothpick	10.00–12.50	
	#6 Electric beater	20.00–25.00	
Row 2:	#1 Measure cup	75.00–85.00	
	#2-4 Measure cups, ea.	25.00–27.50	
	#5 Syrup	22.50–25.00	
	#6 Cruet	18.00–20.00	
	#7 Ash tray	8.00–10.00	

Row 3:	#1 2-piece reamer	25.00–30.00	
	#2 Reamer pitcher	20.00–25.00	
	#3 2-piece reamer-ribbed pitcher	55.00–60.00	
	#4 2-piece reamer	25.00–27.50	
Row 4:	#1 Reamer, odd shade	15.00–20.00	
	#2 "Coke" bottle green	15.00–20.00	
	#3 Reamer, shade most collected	15.00–20.00	
	#4 Tab-handled reamer	12.00–15.00	
	#5 Tab-handled reamer	12.00–15.00	

Page 67

Row 1:	#1 Canister, glass lid, black	22.00–25.00	
	#2 Canister, Tulip design	12.00–15.00	
	#3 Canister (rabbits, ducks, lambs)	10.00–12.50	
	#4 Checkerboard sugar	18.00–20.00	
	#5 Same, flour	20.00–22.50	
Row 2:	#1-4 Shakers, black, ea.	6.00– 7.00	
	#5-7 Shakers, red, ea.	7.00– 8.00	
	#8 Shaker, green	4.00– 5.00	
	#9 Crisscross, 5¼" bowl	7.50– 8.50	
Row 3:	#1 Canister, screw-on lid, green	12.50–15.00	

Row 3:	(Continued)		
	#2 Fire-King, 4⅞" bowl, green	2.50– 3.50	
	#3 Same, 6", red	3.50– 4.50	
	Same 7¼" (not shown)	4.50– 5.00	
	#4 Same, 8⅜", blue	5.50– 6.50	
Row 4:	#1-4 Shakers, ea	4.00– 5.00	
	#5 Bowl, 10¼"	12.00–15.00	
	#6 Syrup, green rings	10.00–12.50	
	#7 Marmalade, red ring w/spoon	7.00– 9.00	

PINK

That pair of embossed salt and pepper shakers on page 72 Row 5 have been reproduced in pink, green, and cobalt blue; the latter was never made originally. See Reproduction Section on pages 236-237 for items with asterisk.

Some of the pink items you need to watch for include: "Tricia" reamer (page 69 Row 4, # 4); Paramount napkin holder (page 71 Row 2, #2); "Ming" reamer (page 71 Row 3, #3) and the dispenser mentioned in the next paragraph. I imagine that you could look at the prices and surmise that on your own.

It turns out that the "so-called" sugar dispenser shown on page 69 Row 4, #5 and (shown complete on page 71 Row 2, #1) is a liquid dispenser for syrup or soap.

Row 1:	#1	Hex Optic stack set, Jeannette; base ($12.50–15.00);	
		lid ($18.00–20.00)	55.00– 65.00
	#2	Hex Optic flat-rim mixing bowl, 9"	22.00– 25.00
		Same, 10" (not shown)	25.00– 27.50
		Same, 8¼" (not shown)	18.00– 20.00
		Same, 7¼" (not shown)	14.00– 16.00
	#3	Hex Optic ruffled-edge mixing bowl, 8¼"	20.00– 22.50
		Same, 10½" (not shown)	25.00– 27.50
		Same, 6" (not shown)	18.00– 20.00
	#4	Ice bucket w/lid, Fry	175.00–200.00
Row 2:	#1	Butter box, 2 lb. embossed "B," Jeannette	140.00–160.00
	#2	Round salt	150.00–165.00
	#3, 4	Flat Jennyware shakers, pr.	55.00– 60.00
	#5	Tumbler	8.00– 10.00
	#6	Cruet	30.00– 35.00
	#7	Barber bottle	15.00– 17.50
Row 3:	#1, 2	Moisture proof shakers, pr.	150.00–165.00
	#3	Reamer, probably foreign	40.00– 45.00
		Same, sun-colored amethyst (not shown)	35.00– 45.00
		Same, crystal (not shown)	20.00– 25.00
	#4	Tumbler, imprinted Mission Juice	25.00– 30.00
	#5, 6	Quilted refrigerator jars, w/lid 8 oz.	25.00– 27.50
		4 oz.	17.50– 20.00
	#7	Stack sugar, creamer and lid	40.00– 50.00
	#8	Same only with place for salt and pepper	35.00– 40.00
		Set w/salt and pepper on above	60.00– 75.00
Row 4:	#1	MacBeth Evans stack set	50.00– 60.00
	#2	Ice bucket	25.00– 30.00
	#3	Ice bucket w/Sterling bear	35.00– 40.00
	#4	Reamer called "Tricia" by collectors	700.00–800.00
	#5	Dispenser w/insert (insert not shown)	150.00–175.00
Row 5:	#1	Reamer, unembossed "Orange Juice Extractor"	185.00–200.00
	#2	Paden City syrup jug	45.00– 50.00
	#3	New Martinsville syrup jug	45.00– 50.00
	#4, 5	Heisey Twist cruet, 2½ oz.	70.00– 75.00
		4 oz.	75.00– 80.00
	#6	Heisey Twist mustard w/spoon	75.00– 80.00
		w/o spoon	40.00– 50.00
	#7	Cambridge syrup	50.00– 55.00
Row 6:	#1	Bowl, 9¾" marked Cambridge	22.00– 25.00
	#2	Bowl, 7¾" plain bottom	10.00– 12.50
	#3	Bowl, 8", concentric rings in bottom	15.00– 18.00
	#4	Butter dish, bow-handled top	50.00– 60.00

PINK (Continued)

Page 71

Row 1: #1   Paden City "Party Line"
           crushed fruit/cookie jar   60.00– 70.00
    #2   Jenkins batter pitcher   125.00–150.00
    #3   Cambridge batter jug for
           waffle set   70.00– 80.00
    #4   Cocktail shaker   65.00– 70.00
Row 2: #1   Dispenser (possibly liquid
           soap or syrup)   150.00–175.00
    #2   Paramount napkin holder
           (U.S. Glass)   350.00–400.00
    #3   U.S. Glass "SHARI" cosmetic
           holder (2 pc.)   125.00–150.00
    #4   Stack set: sugar/creamer/
           plate/shakers   60.00– 75.00

Row 3: #1   Cambridge double gravy boat   25.00– 30.00
    #2   Imperial gravy boat   20.00– 25.00
    #3   Fenton "Ming" 2-piece reamer   500.00–600.00
    #4   Tufglas jello mold   25.00– 30.00
Row 4: #1   Paden City Party Line ice tub   25.00– 30.00
    #2   U.S. Glass 2-cup measure   150.00–175.00
    #3   Cambridge 1-cup measure   200.00–225.00
    #4   Stack sugar/creamer/lid   45.00– 50.00
    #5, 6   Curtain tie backs, ea.   8.00– 10.00
Row 5: #1, 2   Curtain tie backs, ea.   11.00– 14.00
    #3   Drawer pull, single   7.00– 10.00
    #4, 5   Single towel rods, 18", ea.   25.00– 30.00
    #6   Double towel rod   30.00– 35.00

Page 72

Hocking Glass Company

Row 1: #1	Pretzel jar	65.00–75.00
#2-4	Canisters, plain, 40 oz.	40.00–50.00
	20 oz. (not shown)	35.00–40.00
	8 oz.	30.00–35.00
#5	Refrigerator dish, 4" x 4", indented handles	15.00–17.50
#6	Measure pitcher, 2 cup, ribbed	35.00–40.00

Federal Glass Company

Row 2: #1-4	Mixing bowl set (4)	45.00–55.00
	9½"	15.00–18.00
	8½"	12.00–15.00
	7½"	10.00–12.00
	6½"	8.00–10.00
Row 3: #1, 2 & 4	Refrigerator dish set (3)	65.00–70.00
	8" x 8"	32.00–35.00
	4" x 8"	20.00–22.50
	4" x 4"	10.00–12.50
#3	Refrigerator dish, 3¾" x 5¾", w/legs	18.00–20.00
#5	Butter dish, ¼ lb.	30.00–32.50
Row 4: #1	Butter dish, 1 lb.	40.00–42.50
#2	4" x 4" vegetable embossed lid (asparagus)	20.00–22.00

Row 4: (Continued)		
	4" x 8" vegetable embossed lid (not shown)	25.00– 30.00
#3, 4	Round refrigerator dish, 4½"	15.00– 20.00
	Same, 5½"	12.00– 15.00
#5	Reamer, Federal	90.00–100.00

Hazel Atlas Glass Company

Row 5: #1, 2	Mixing bowls, 11⅝" (not shown)	20.00– 25.00
	10⅝" (not shown)	20.00– 22.00
	9⅝"	15.00– 18.00
	8½" (not shown)	12.00– 15.00
	7⅝"	10.00– 12.00
	6⅝" (not shown)	8.00– 10.00
#3, 4	Salt or pep, embossed	*40.00– 45.00
#5	Cruet	40.00– 45.00
#6	Milk pitcher	25.00– 30.00
Row 6: #1-4	REST-WELL mixing bowl set (5)	60.00– 70.00
	9½"	17.50– 20.00
	8½"	15.00– 18.00
	7½"	10.00– 12.00
	6½" (not shown)	8.00– 10.00
	5½"	8.00– 10.00

Page 73

Row 1: #1	Utility pitcher	50.00–60.00
#2	Slick-handle measure pitcher	40.00–45.00
#3	Measure cup	50.00–60.00
#4	Cruet	40.00–45.00
#5	Cruet	35.00–40.00
#6	Apothecary jar	22.00–25.00
Row 2: #1	Heisey cigarette and ash tray	65.00–75.00
#2	Cruet set	75.00–80.00
#3	Mixing bowl, 7"	14.00–16.00
	Same, 5"	10.00–12.50
	Same, 9"	18.00–20.00
#4	Mug, "Adams Rib"	18.00–20.00
#5	Ice pail	18.00–20.00
Row 3: #1	Round crock, 8", lid fits outside	35.00–40.00
#2	Same, 6½"	25.00–30.00
#3	Round refrigerator dish, tab handle	25.00–30.00

Row 3: (Continued)		
#4	"Kompakt" dish unit	40.00–50.00
Row 4: #1	Slick-handle mixing bowl, 8¾" w/lid, spouted	40.00–45.00
	Same w/o lid	15.00–20.00
#2	Slick-handle mixing bowl, 9", (2 handles, spouted)	22.00–25.00
	Same w/lid	40.00–45.00
#3	Slick handle bowl, 7½", spouted, "D&B" embossed	20.00–25.00
Row 5: #1	Slick handle 9" concentric ring bowl	20.00–22.00
	Same, w/lid	32.00–35.00
#2	Snowflake cake plate	20.00–22.00
#3	2-handle bowl, no spout, 9"	20.00–22.00

RED, TRANSPARENT and FIRED-ON COLORS

I've seen few red kitchens around, but red is a dramatic accent color; so there is a lot of demand for the red pieces shown here and on the next page. Fired-on colors really photograph nicely as you can see on page 77.

Page 75

Row 1:	#1	Boot cocktail shaker	250.00–300.00
	#2	Silex coffee pot	175.00–200.00
	#3	Decanter w/shot glass stopper	100.00–110.00
Row 2:	#1	Cocktail shaker	35.00– 40.00
	#2	3 oz. tumbler that goes w/#1	4.00– 6.00
	#3	Barbell cocktail shaker (possibly New Martinsville)	85.00– 95.00

Row 2:	(Continued)		
	#4	Duncan Miller cocktail shaker	50.00– 55.00
	#5	Cocktail shaker	40.00– 50.00
Row 3:	#1	McKee batter pitcher	75.00– 85.00
	#2	Batter pitcher w/tray	150.00–175.00
	#3, 4	Tumble-up set	150.00–175.00

Page 76

Row 1:	#1	Hocking tumbler w/Old Reliable tea bags	10.00– 12.00
	#2, 3	Hocking water bottles, plain or ribbed	75.00– 85.00
	#4	Food chopper	20.00– 25.00
	#5	Strawholder (possibly 60's)	150.00–200.00
	#6	Hocking 24 oz. beater jar	40.00– 45.00
Row 2:	#1	Cambridge "Mt. Vernon" ice bucket	75.00– 85.00
	#2	Hocking ice bucket	30.00– 35.00
	#3	Cruet	100.00–120.00
	#4	Sugar shaker (maybe 60's)	125.00–150.00
	#5, 6	Wheaton Nuline shakers, pr.	40.00– 50.00
	#7, 8	Hocking shakers (possibly 60's), pr.	35.00– 45.00

Row 3:	#1	Imperial gravy & platter	150.00–175.00
	#2	Butter w/crystal top	105.00–120.00
	#3	Mixing bowl set (3)	190.00–220.00
		9¼"	90.00–100.00
		7¾"	60.00– 70.00
		6½"	40.00– 50.00
Row 4:	#1	Percolator top	15.00– 17.50
	#2	Knob escutcheon plate for door knob	10.00– 12.00
	#3	Double drawer pull	35.00– 45.00
	#4	Single drawer pull	20.00– 25.00
	#5, 6	Curtain rings, ea.	10.00– 12.00
	#7, 8	Feathered curtain tie backs, pr.	25.00– 35.00
Row 5:	#1	Trivet	40.00– 50.00
	#2	Tray (possibly for a New Martinsville set)	45.00– 50.00
	#3, 4	Fork & spoon set	175.00–200.00

Page 77

Row 1:	#1, 2	Rooster decanter w/4 shots	35.00–40.00
	#3	Sugar shaker (Gemco)	18.00–20.00
	#4	Canister, blue	15.00–18.00
	#5	Rooster canister, small	20.00–25.00
	#6	Same, medium	25.00–30.00
	#7	Same, large	35.00–40.00
Row 2:	#1	Measure, 2 cup	10.00–12.00
	#2	Pyrex, refrigerator jar, 3½" x 4¾"	4.00– 5.00
	#3	Hazel Atlas cup, green	32.00–35.00
	#4	Same, red	35.00–40.00
	#5, 6	Hocking ribbed shakers, blue, ea.	8.00–10.00
Row 3:	#1-3	Hocking, yellow, ea.	7.00– 9.00
	#4-6	Same, blue, ea.	10.00–12.00
	#7-10	Same, green, ea.	9.00–11.00

Row 4:	#1-5	Roman arch side panel, ea.	8.00–10.00
	#6	Glasbake, red cup	25.00–30.00
	#7, 8	Shakers, ea	4.00– 5.00
	#9	Reamer, tab handle, red	12.00–15.00
Row 5:	#1	Oval 7" jar, black	15.00–18.00
	#2, 3	Shaker (go with #1-3 in Row 4)	5.00– 6.00
	#4	Rolling pin, white	25.00–30.00
Row 6:	#1	Mustard (Gemco set)	4.00– 5.00
	#2	Salt bowl, same	8.00–10.00
	#3	Sugar shaker, same	15.00–20.00
	#4	Hazel Atlas sugar canister	25.00–30.00
	#5	Same, coffee	20.00–25.00
	#6	Same, tea	18.00–20.00
	#7	Hocking tea canister	12.50–15.00

FIRED-ON COLORS (Continued)

Isn't this a super photo! I hope it shows the awesome display potential for collecting fired-on colors, which are abundantly available! Red and green items have traditionally been my best sellers over the years.

The blue windmill drippings jar in Row 2 was re-photographed since it had been turned so you could not see the word "Drippings" in the last book. Much to my chagrin, upon viewing the new photographs from a six day marathon photo shoot last October, the "Drippings" label had been turned to the back again! Someday we will get it right.

Page 79

Row 1:	#1-#4	Shakers, ea.	5.00– 6.00
	#5	Cup w/red handle	4.00– 5.00
	#6	Black shaker	8.00–10.00
	#7	Small sugar shaker	12.00–14.00
	#8	Small striped canister	5.00– 6.00
Row 2:	#1	Dutch bowl, 7"	8.00–10.00
	#2	Dutch cereal, 5"	6.00– 8.00
	#3	Oil or vinegar bottle	8.00–10.00
	#4	Apothecary jar	10.00–12.00
	#5	Drippings jar (turned backwards)	30.00–35.00
	#6	Glasbake measure pitcher	25.00–30.00
Row 3:	#1	Hazel Atlas flour canister (goes w/set page 77 Row 6)	25.00–30.00
	#2,6	Syrup, ea.	12.50–15.00
	#3	Batter bowl	12.50–15.00
	#4	Knobs, ea.	6.00– 8.00
	#4	Carafe	4.00– 5.00
Row 4:	#1-4	Pyrex bowl set	20.00–28.00
	#1	Yellow	8.00–10.00
	#2	Red	6.00– 8.00
	#3	Green	4.00– 6.00
	#4	Blue	2.00– 4.00
Row 5:	#1,2	Multi-colored soup cups, ea.	2.50– 4.00
	#3	Pyrex 3½" x 4¾" yellow refrigerator dish	3.00– 4.00
	#4	Pyrex 4¼" x 6¾" blue refrigerator dish	5.00– 7.00
	#5	Cobalt tumbler w/red, white Dutch scene	12.50–15.00
	#6	Crystal pitcher w/Dutch scene	18.00–20.00
	#7	Same as #4, red	6.00– 8.00
	#8	Same as #3, orange	3.00– 4.00
	#9	Pyrex 7" x 9", yellow refrigerator dish	8.00–10.00

WHITE

White kitchenware is very versatile in a decorating scheme and more abundant than many colors! Prices reflect that abundance; so, today's collectors are using this color in their kitchens.

The napkin holder in the bottom row on Page 81 is marked "HY-G NAPKINS." It is the only one I have seen!

Page 81

Row 1: #1,2 Salt and "white pepper" pr. 12.00–15.00
#3   Musketeer "Allspice"   10.00–12.00
#4,5 Salt and pepper "4 Rings," pr. 12.00–15.00
#6   "Home Soap Company" shaker
#7   "Red Tulips" Vitrock grease jar 20.00–25.00
#8,10 "Red Tulips" salt or pepper, ea. 10.00–12.50
#9   "Red Tulips" sugar   15.00–17.50

Row 2: #1   Chicken sherbet   10.00–12.50
#2,3 Salt and pepper pr.   10.00–12.00
#4   Anchor Hocking mug,
     chicken decal   5.00– 6.00
#5   Hazel Atlas mug, chef scene 8.00–10.00
#6,7 Drawer pulls, ea.   4.00– 5.00
#8   McKee "FRIZZ" bowl (Just
     1. Chill; 2. Whip; 3. Freeze) 30.00–35.00

Row 3: #1-18 Griffith's shakers, (w/label) ea. 1.50–2.50
#1-18 Griffith's shakers, (wo/label) ea. 1.00–1.25

Row 4: #1   Hazel Atlas "Dutch, tulips,
     windmills" plate (goes with
     set shown on page 231) 6.00– 8.00
#2   Same, cup and saucer 12.50– 15.00
#3   Rooster bowl   5.00– 6.00
#4   McKee, Glasbake coffee pot 30.00– 35.00
#5   Hazel Atlas, 4 cup measure,
     stippled exterior   *18.00– 20.00

Row 5: #1,2 Canisters, decaled cherry
     or vegetables, ea.   15.00– 17.50
#3   Canisters, decaled vegetables 14.00– 16.00
#4   Hazel Atlas "Dots" tumbler 12.50– 15.00
#5   Syrup   30.00– 35.00
#3   Napkin holder marked
     "HY-G NAPKINS"   125.00–150.00

* BEWARE REPRODUCTIONS

Page 82   McKee Glass Company

Row 1: #1-4 Canister, 48 oz., ea   45.00– 50.00
#5-8 Large shakers, ea   40.00– 45.00

Row 2: #1-4 Shakers, ea.   10.00– 12.00
#5,6 Salt, pepper, ea.   12.00– 15.00
#7,8 Flour, sugar, ea.   20.00– 22.00
#9   Canister, same design 50.00– 60.00
#10 Dots 48 oz. canister 40.00– 50.00

Row 3: #1   Grapefruit reamer 250.00–350.00
#2   Tea w/lid   25.00– 30.00
#3   Bowl, 9" w/decal   20.00– 25.00
#4   2 cup measure w/decal 25.00– 30.00

Row 4: #1   Bowl, 9"   12.00– 15.00
#2,3 Shakers (good lettering!) 12.00– 15.00
#4   Reamer, small   18.00– 20.00
#5   Sunkist reamer   7.00– 10.00

Row 5: #1   Water dispenser   90.00–110.00
#2   Glasbak measure cup 45.00– 50.00
#3   Shakers, salt   10.00– 12.00
#4,5 Shaker, flour or sugar 18.00– 20.00
#6   Diamond Check shaker 15.00– 17.50

Page 83   Hocking Glass Company Vitrock

Row 1: #1   Canister w/glass lid
     (rare)   75.00–85.00
#2   Canister, 20 oz. screw-on
     lid   22.50–25.00
#3   Shaker   8.00–10.00
#4-5 Mixing bowl, 6¾"   6.00– 8.00
     Same, 7½" (not shown) 8.00–10.00
     Same, 8½" (not shown) 10.00–12.50
     Same, 9½" (not shown) 12.50–15.00
     Same, 10¼" (not shown) 18.00–20.00
     Same, 11¼"   22.50–25.00

Row 2: #1   "Blue Circle" flour   25.00–27.50
#2-5 Same, shakers, ea.   10.00–12.00
#6,7 "Black Circle" shakers, ea. 10.00–12.00

Row 3: #1   Grease w/o label   20.00–22.00
     Same, w/label   20.00–25.00
#2   2 cup measure w/lid 30.00–40.00
#3   Reamer   18.00–20.00
#4   Bowl, 10", red trim   20.00–22.00

Row 4: #1-3 "Red Circle" w/screw-on
     lids   35.00–40.00
#4-6 Same, shakers, ea.   10.00–12.00

Row 5: #1   "Red Circle w/flowers,"
     canister w/screw-on lid 30.00–35.00
#2   Tab handle reamer   75.00–95.00
#3   4" x 4" refrigerator dish 15.00–18.00
#4   8" x 8" refrigerator dish 30.00–32.50

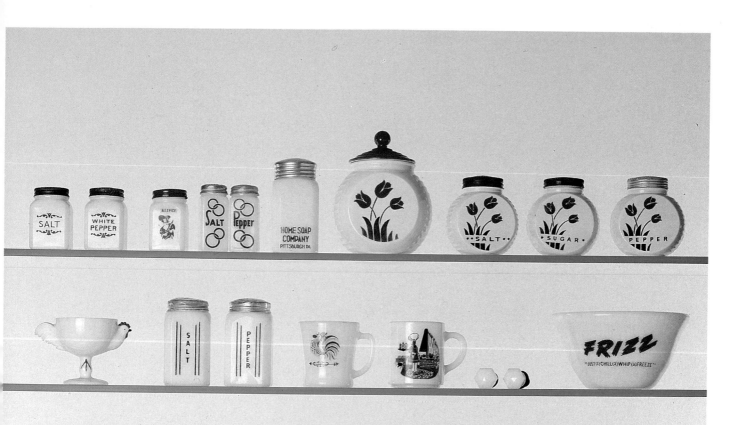

YELLOW, OPAQUE, and TRANSPARENT, McKee, Hocking and Others

McKee's opaque yellow is called "Seville." This color is sometimes confused with Custard by beginning collectors. Custard leans to the white with a beige tint while "Seville" **is** yellow. Page 85 gives a representative example of this color that can be compared to Hocking's opaque yellow shown on page 86. Even though Hocking's yellow is more rare, there are fewer collectors; and that limits its price potential. Most yellow opaque pieces are found with black lettering, but there are exceptions to that rule. Some Hocking pieces have been seen with green lettering! Price the cookie jar below for $250.00 – 300.00.

Page 85 McKee Glass Company

Row 1:	#1	Pinch decanter	100.00–110.00
	#2	Measure, 4 cup, no handle	350.00–400.00
	#3	Measure, 4 cup, ftd. w/handle	115.00–130.00
	#4	4 cup dry measure (mug)	150.00–200.00
Row 2:	#1	Bottoms down mug	125.00–135.00
	#2	Measure, 2 cup	30.00– 35.00
	#3-9	Salt or pepper, ea.	12.00– 15.00
		Flour or sugar, ea.	16.00– 18.00

Row 3:	#1	Grapefruit reamer	210.00–225.00
	#2	Sunkist reamer	45.00– 55.00
	#3	Refrigerator dish, 7¼" square	30.00– 35.00
Row 4:	#1	Butter dish	65.00– 75.00
	#2	4" x 5" refrigerator dish	15.00– 18.00
	#3	Measure cup, 2 spout	175.00–195.00
	#4	Bowl, 4¼"	10.00– 12.00
Row 5:	#1	Mixing bowl, 9¼"	22.50– 25.00
	#2	Same, 7½"	18.00– 20.00
	#3,4	Canister, 48 oz., ea.	55.00– 60.00

Page 86 Hocking Glass Company

Row 1:	#1-3	Canister, 40 oz., ea.	65.00–75.00
	#4,5	Canister, 20 oz., ea.	30.00–35.00
Row 2:	#1	Refrigerator jar, 4" x 4"	12.00–15.00
		Same, w/lid	18.00–20.00
	#2,3	Shaker, flour or sugar	15.00–18.00
	#4	Refrigerator dish, 6" x 6"	20.00–22.50

Row 3:	#1	Measure pitcher	175.00–200.00
	#2	Batter bowl	75.00– 85.00
Row 4:	#1	Refrigerator dish, 8" x 8"	40.00– 50.00
	#2, 4	Salt or pepper	12.00– 14.00
	#3	Grease jar	40.00– 45.00

Yellow Transparent
Page 87

Row 1:	#1	Fenton ice bucket	125.00–135.00
	#2	U.S. Glass reamer pitcher	650.00–750.00
	#3	Glass for above set	15.00– 17.50
	#4	Fostoria ice bucket	30.00– 35.00
	#5	Fostoria oil and vinegar	65.00– 75.00
	#6	Fostoria "Mayfair" cruet	75.00– 85.00
Row 2:	#1	Fostoria oil and vinegar	45.00– 50.00
	#2	Fostoria "Mayfair" syrup & liner	65.00– 70.00
	#3	Sugar shaker	250.00–300.00
	#4	Hazel Atlas 2 cup reamer set	275.00–300.00
	#5	Hazel Atlas mug	30.00– 35.00
	#6	Duncan "Festive" gravy & ladle	40.00– 50.00
Row 3:	#1	Heisey syrup	75.00– 85.00
	#2	Heisey "Old Sandwich"	85.00– 95.00
	#3	Hazel Atlas 1 cup measure, 3 spout	225.00–250.00
	#4	Hazel Atlas egg cup	3.00– 5.00
	#5	Canning funnel "C.W. Hart," Troy, N.Y.	35.00– 45.00
	#6	Hazel Atlas refrigerator dish 4½" x 5"	30.00– 35.00
Row 4:	#1	Hazel Atlas REST-WELL, mixing bowl, 8¾"	35.00– 40.00
	#2	Same, 7¾"	30.00– 35.00

Row 4:	(Continued)		
	#3	Same, 6¾"	22.00–25.00
	#4	Same, 5¾"	18.00–20.00
Row 5:	#1	U.S. Glass slick handled batter bowl	30.00–35.00
	#2	Soap dish	18.00–20.00
	#3	Cambridge sugar cube tray	65.00–75.00
	#4	Spoon, salad size	30.00–35.00
	#5	Spoon, regular size	25.00–30.00

Part 2 Kitchen Items

BATTER JUGS and BATTER BOWLS

Batter jugs were usually made in sets consisting of a batter jug and lid, syrup and lid and drip tray. Although these sets were made by several different companies in a myriad of colors, cobalt blue and red are the most popular colors with collectors.

Page 91 shows a collection of batter bowls. They came in many shapes and sizes, although all those shown were made by Hocking. The "Mayfair" blue in Row 2 and the "Turquoise Blue" in Row 4 are most coveted by collectors. It took us four years to find the "Turquoise Blue" when we were collecting that color.

The Hocking canister in Row 3 was a late arrival, and since this was an all Hocking page I included it there. The top shows that "ARCO" Coffee was in the jar; but when empty, the jar was to become your cookies' home.

Page 89

Row 1:	#1	Paden City crystal w/black lids set	125.00–150.00
	#2	Paden City black set	250.00–275.00
	#3	Paden City pink w/black tray set	150.00–175.00
Row 2:	#1	Paden City syrup	50.00– 60.00
	#2	Paden City batter jug	60.00– 70.00
	#3	Paden City milk jug	55.00– 65.00
	#4	Paden City green batter jug	65.00– 75.00
	#5	Cambridge pink batter jug for waffle set	75.00– 85.00
	#6	Cambridge amber syrup jug	50.00– 55.00

Row 3:	#1	Jenkins #570 green batter jug	125.00–135.00
	#2	Green batter jug	85.00– 95.00
	#3	Square green batter jug	100.00–110.00
	#4	Jenkins green batter jug	200.00–225.00
Row 4:	#1	Jenkins pink batter jug	115.00–135.00
	#2	Jeannette Jadite (bottom only- $50.00)	200.00–250.00
	#3	Liberty "American Pioneer" batter jug	150.00–165.00
	#4	Same, syrup jug	125.00–140.00

Page 90

Row 1:	#1	New Martinsville cobalt blue batter set	300.00–350.00
	#2	Same, amber	150.00–175.00
	#3	Red batter jug & liner	150.00–175.00
Row 2:	#1	New Martinsville green batter jug	65.00– 75.00
	#2	Same, syrup jug	60.00– 65.00
	#3	New Martinsville crystal batter w/green top	30.00– 40.00

Row 2:	(Continued)		
	#4	New Martinsville pink syrup jug	40.00– 50.00
Row 3:	#1	McKee black batter	100.00–110.00
	#2	Same, white	60.00– 65.00
	#3	Same, blue	90.00–100.00
	#4	Same, red	75.00– 85.00

Page 91 All Anchor Hocking Glass Company

Row 1:	#1	Ribbed green	20.00– 25.00
	#2	Opaque yellow	75.00– 85.00
Row 2:	#1	Ribbed crystal	10.00– 12.00
	#2	Spiraled green	20.00– 22.00
	#3	"Mayfair" blue	150.00–175.00

Row 3:	#1	Cookie jar w/coffee lid	40.00– 45.00
	#2	Fire-King (peach/grape)	15.00– 18.00
Row 4:	#1	Same, Jadite	15.00– 18.00
	#2	Same, "Turquoise Blue"	135.00–150.00

BUTTER DISHES, CHEESE DISHES, and CANISTERS

Butter dishes can be found in several sizes and shapes from quarter pound to two pounds. Many were premium items as indicated by the advertising found imprinted or embossed on them. In Row 2, #4 on page 93, the top says "Ask for Iowa creamery butter, always good!" So many older canisters are finding their way into today's kitchens that I have included a page of some odd ones. After all, it was canisters with screw-on lids that Cathy began buying 15 years ago that eventually evolved into this book.

Page 93

Row 1:	#1	Custard, McKee	35.00– 40.00
	#2	Skokie green, McKee	40.00– 45.00
	#3	Seville yellow, McKee	60.00– 65.00
Row 2:	#1	Ships, McKee	22.00– 25.00
	#2	Red Dots	100.00–125.00
	#3	Delphite, McKee	225.00–250.00
	#4	Jadite bottom, metal top ad	20.00– 25.00
Row 3:	#1,2	Amber ¼ lb., Federal, ea.	25.00– 30.00
	#3	Crystal frosted, ¼ lb. Federal	12.00– 15.00
	#4	Amber 1 lb., Federal	30.00– 35.00
	#5	Amber tub, Federal	25.00– 30.00
Row 4:	**Jeannette** tops embossed "BUTTER"		
	#1	Delphite,	225.00–250.00

Row 4:	(Continued)		
	#2	Jadite, dark,	40.00– 45.00
	#3	Jadite, light,	35.00– 40.00
	#4	Green,	35.00– 40.00
	#5	Pink, (all pink)	55.00– 60.00
Row 5:	#1	Ultra-marine, "Jennyware"	125.00–150.00
	#2	Same, crystal	50.00– 60.00
	#3	Same, pink	110.00–125.00
	#4	Pink, embossed Scotty	35.00– 40.00
Row 6:	#1	Green, embossed "B," 2 lb.	125.00–150.00
	#2	Green, "Hex Optic"	60.00– 65.00
	#3	Pink, embossed "B," 2 lb.	140.00–160.00

Page 94

Row 1:	#1	Green, unknown	40.00– 45.00
	#2	Green, Hocking	25.00– 30.00
	#3	Green, "Block Optic," Hocking	40.00– 45.00
Row 2:	#1	Green, unknown	40.00– 50.00
	#2	Green "Clambroth," Hocking	65.00– 75.00
	#3	Green, unknown	30.00– 35.00
	#4	Refrigerator dish (sold as butter)	15.00– 18.00
Row 3:	**Hazel Atlas** tops embossed "BUTTER COVER"		
	#1	Green	35.00– 40.00
	#2	Crystal	18.00– 22.00
	#3	White	20.00– 25.00

Row 3:	(Continued)		
	#4	Cobalt blue	190.00–215.00
Row 4:	#1, 3	"Crisscross," 1 lb., green or pink	35.00– 40.00
	#2	Same, crystal	18.00– 20.00
	#4	Same, cobalt blue	85.00– 95.00
Row 5:	#1, 3	Same, ¼ lb., green or pink	35.00– 40.00
	#2	Same, crystal	15.00– 18.00
	#4	Same, cobalt blue	85.00– 95.00
Row 6:	#1	"Sanitary Refrigerator Jar"	135.00–150.00
	#2	Cheese, blue (foreign?)	125.00–140.00
	#3	"Hot & Cold" embossed	45.00– 50.00
	#4	Cheese "Sanitary Preserver"	35.00– 40.00

Page 95

Row 1:	#1	Fleur-de-lis pepper	6.00– 7.00
	#2	Fleur-de-lis salt	8.00–10.00
	#3-5	Fleur-de-lis coffee, sugar, flour, ea.	20.00–22.50
	#6	Large canister w/o label	4.00– 5.00
	#7	Small canister w/o label	1.00– 1.50
Row 2:	#1	Teal stacking jar set	25.00–30.00
	#2	Sugar shaker	20.00–22.00
	#3-7	Spice canisters (match canisters in Row 1), ea.	5.00– 6.00
	#8	Refrigerator container	5.00– 6.00
	#9	Teal canister	25.00–30.00
Row 3:	#1	Canister, 64 oz.	15.00–17.50

Row 3:	(Continued)		
	#2	Canister, 32 oz.	11.00–12.50
	#3-5	Canister, 8 oz., ea.	5.00– 6.00
	#6	Canister, 16 oz., "Three Bears"	12.50–15.00
Row 4:	#1,2	Canister white w/Mexican decal, ea.	10.00–12.50
	#3	Canister, 128 oz.	40.00–45.00
	#4	Hazel Atlas flour canister	25.00–30.00
Row 5:	#1	"Clambroth" white large canister	35.00–40.00
	#2	Same, medium	25.00–30.00
	#3	Same, small	15.00–17.50
	#4	L.E.Smith jar	50.00–55.00
	#5	L.E.Smith jar, larger version	60.00–65.00

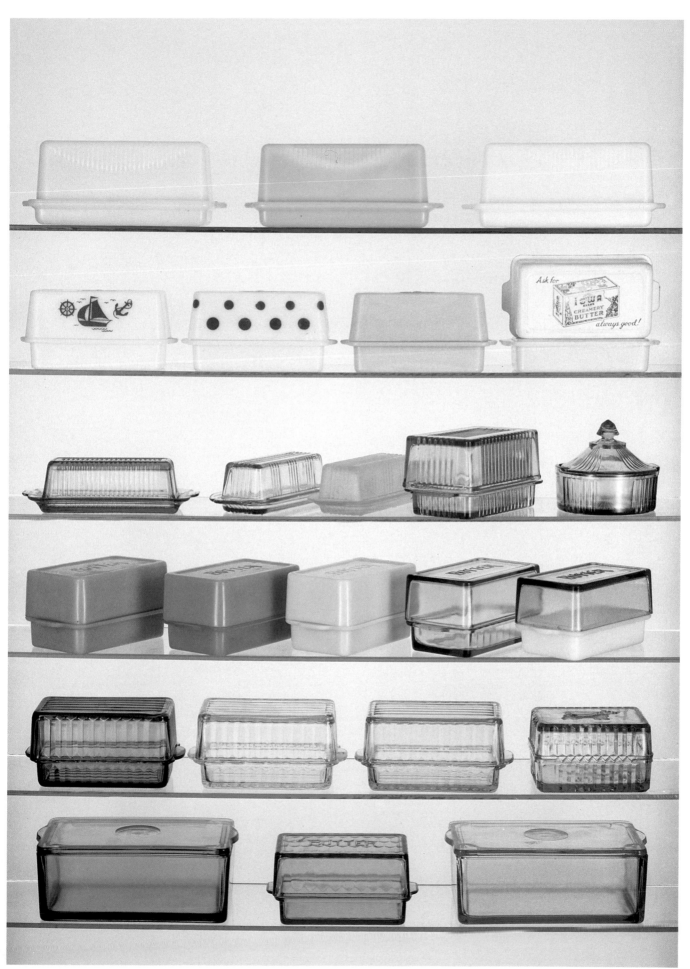

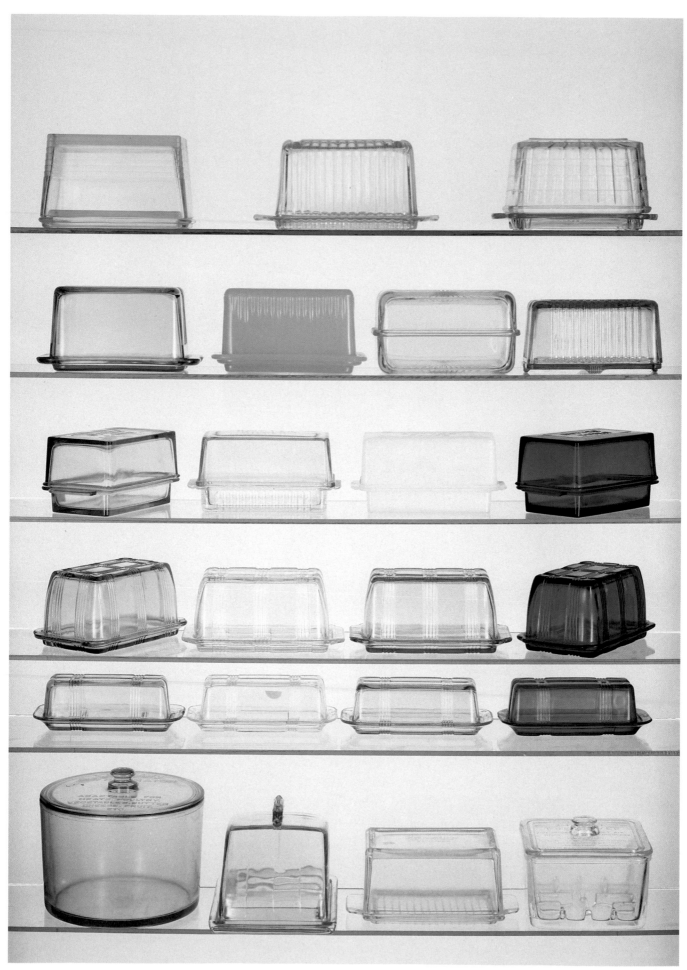

CRUETS and DISPENSERS (Refrigerator Type)

Page 97

Row 1: #1   Fostoria yellow "Trojan" 225.00–250.00
     #2   Fostoria blue "Fairfax,"
        w/stopper   125.00–150.00
     #3   Fostoria amber "Fairfax,"
        w/stopper   75.00– 85.00
     #4   Fostoria green "Mayfair"   85.00– 95.00
     #5   Same, yellow, w/stopper 75.00– 85.00
Row 2: #1   Fostoria "Colony"   35.00– 40.00
     #2   Fostoria yellow "Baroque,"
        w/stopper   175.00–200.00
     #3   Paden City pink #210
        line   40.00– 50.00
     #4   Same, green   45.00– 50.00
     #5   Jadite "Vinegar"   150.00–175.00
Row 3: #1   U.S. Glass (?) set on tray 75.00– 80.00
     #2   Imperial blue (not Heisey
        experimental blue)   75.00– 85.00
     #3   Same as #1, pink   75.00– 80.00

Row 3: (Continued)
     #4   Pink   40.00–45.00
Row 4: #1   U.S. Glass green   40.00–45.00
     #2   Same, crystal   15.00–18.00
     #3   Same, pink   35.00–40.00
     #4   Imperial, pink   30.00–35.00
     #5   New Martinsville "Janice"
        blue   55.00–65.00
     #6   New Martinsville "Radiance"
        crystal   15.00–20.00
Row 5: #1   Cambridge green   35.00–40.00
     #2   Same, amber   32.00–35.00
     #3   Cambridge, "Caprice"
        blue   60.00–70.00
     #4   Cambridge, "Apple Blos-
        som" pink   85.00–95.00
     #5   Cambridge, amber in
        Faberware   15.00–20.00

Page 98

Row 1: #1   Imperial "Canary Yellow"
        (vaseline)   45.00– 50.00
     #2   Imperial green   35.00– 40.00
     #3   Imperial "Cape Cod"   22.00– 25.00
     #4   Imperial ribbed & beaded,
        pink   35.00– 40.00
     #5   Same, no beads   35.00– 40.00
     #6   Heisey, crystal   30.00– 35.00
Row 2: #1   Lancaster Glass Company,
        yellow   60.00– 65.00
     #2   Same, green   55.00– 65.00
     #3   Pink blown (probably
        foreign)   40.00– 50.00
     #4   Imperial pink   45.00– 50.00
     #5   Fostoria "Garland"   50.00– 60.00
     #6   Amber   30.00– 35.00
Row 3: #1   Heisey "Old Sandwich"
        w/stopper   85.00– 95.00
     #2   Heisey "Yeoman"   50.00– 60.00
     #3   Heisey "Twist," 4 oz.,
        "Moongleam" green   75.00– 85.00

Row 3: (Continued)
     #4   Same, "Flamingo" pink   75.00– 80.00
     #5   Same, 2½ oz.   70.00– 75.00
     #6   Imperial "Cape Cod"   15.00– 20.00
     #7   Duncan "Caribbean" blue 65.00– 75.00
Row 4: #1   Duncan "Canterbury"   20.00– 25.00
     #2   Red   100.00–120.00
     #3   Green   40.00– 50.00
     #4   Imperial's "Verde" green
        from Heisey "Crystolite"
        mold   15.00– 20.00
     #5   Hazel Atlas green   30.00– 35.00
     #6   Same, pink   40.00– 45.00
Row 5: #1, 2 U.S. Glass (?) dark
        green, ea.   35.00– 40.00
     #3   Pink   30.00– 35.00
     #4   Green   30.00– 35.00
     #5   Crystal   18.00– 20.00
     #6   Hocking green   18.00– 20.00

Page 99

Row 1: #1   L.E. Smith cobalt blue
        water dispenser   350.00–400.00
     #2   Same, light blue   200.00–225.00
     #3   McKee white dispenser   90.00–110.00
Row 2: #1   McKee Jade Green dis-
        penser, 5¼" tall   150.00–175.00
     #2   McKee Jade Green
        dispenser   100.00–115.00

Row 2: (Continued)
     #3   McKee custard dispenser 110.00–125.00
Row 3: #1   McKee w/Jade Green
        top   120.00–135.00
     #2   Sneath Glass Co. green
        clambroth w/crystal top 55.00– 65.00
     #3   Water dispenser, Jade
        Green top   45.00– 55.00

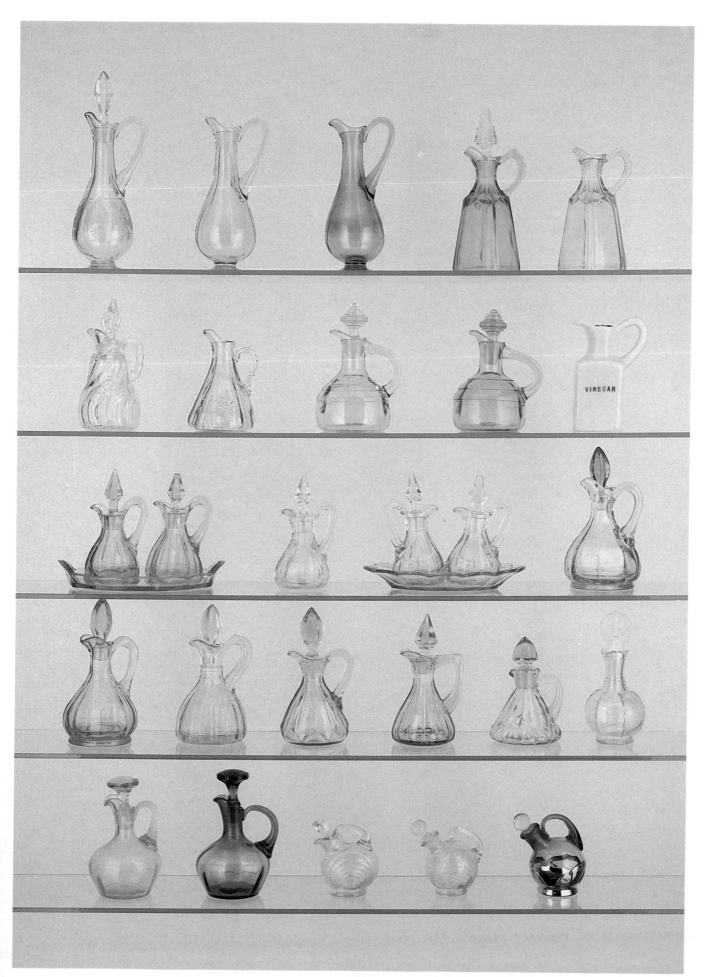

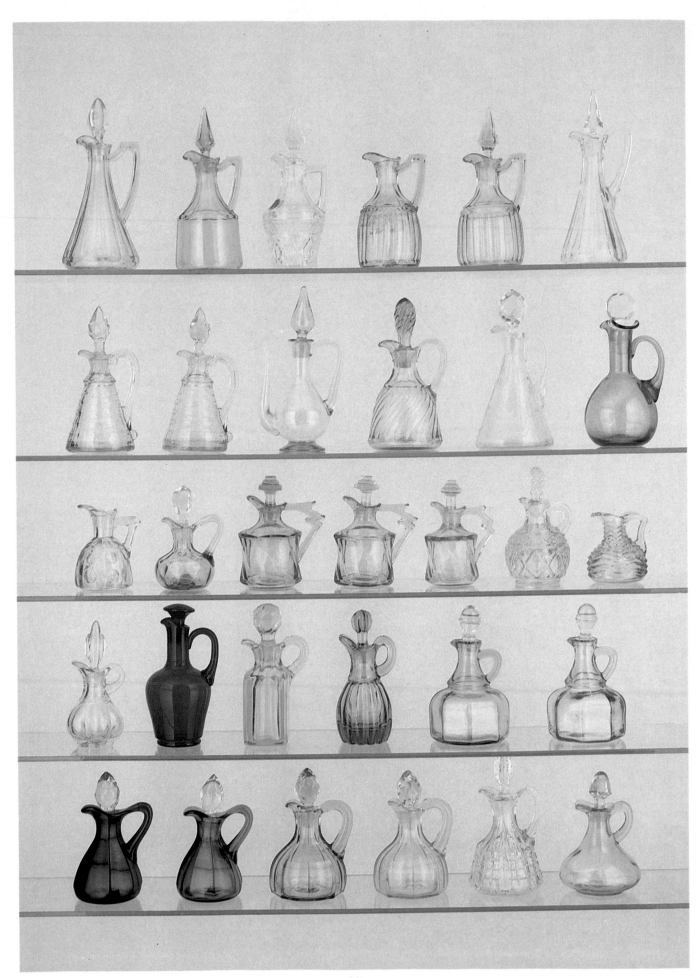

DISPENSERS, Drink and Juice

Antique shows that feature old advertising items are among the best places to find kitchenware collectibles. In days past, that was where I bought many of my colored straw holders as well as other kitchen related collectibles. Today, all that has changed is advertising dealers now attend Depression Glass shows to buy our Kitchenware to take to their shows. I miss the $150.00–200.00 prices for green straw jars at those shows!

The popularity of these remnants from restaurant and soda fountain days is awesome as my son used to say! Advertising shows draw collectors with megabucks. There are usually four or five of these dispensers at one of the larger shows. Rarely are there any unsold, if priced fairly, when it is over. One impediment, when it comes to exhibiting them, is size. Because of lingering nostalgic memories, most are finding homes on antique bars in the den or game room.

Page 101

Row 1:	#1	Crystal and Green (no name)	200.00–250.00
	#2	Samovar, green w/copper holder	175.00–200.00
Row 2:	#1	"Middleby" quality	150.00–175.00
	#2	"Orange Crush" type	175.00–200.00
	#3	Manufactured by E.B. Evans Co Philadelphia 33, Pa	200.00–225.00

Page 102

Row 1:	#1	Samovar yellow (possibly Paden City)	250.00–300.00
	#2	Mission Orange	250.00–300.00
	#3	Mission Grapefruit	300.00–325.00
Row 2:	#1	Paden City percolator, 3 piece, green	300.00–325.00
		Amber (not shown)	250.00–275.00
	#2	Mission Real Fruit Juice (pink)	175.00–200.00
	#3	Mission Real Fruit Juice (green)	175.00–200.00

Page 103

Row 1:	#1	Bireley's Orange Juice	350.00–375.00
	#2	Amber barrel and green base	275.00–300.00
	#3	Samovar green (possibly Paden City)	250.00–300.00
Row 2:	#1	Orange Crush	225.00–250.00

103

ICE BUCKETS & BEVERAGE DISPENSERS

The cobalt blue and amethyst beverage dispensers (top row of page 105) are Cambridge glass. Some have been found on a matching color round tray; but, so far, no sets have been found with any type of drinking vessel. They are marked on the bottom: "The American Thermos Bottle Co., Norwich, Conn. U.S.A.; Genuine Thermos Reg. U.S. Patent Office; Pat. App'd For: Vacuum Bottle." The metal bottle shown with these probably proved to be more durable!

Collectors of ice buckets tell me the first fifty buckets are found rather easily; the next fifty come with some difficulty; and once you have approximately one hundred, you can no longer find those you don't already own or the room to display them! I've seen photos of some super collections; and most of them have been very artfully displayed.

Page 105

Row 1:	#1	Cambridge cobalt blue Thermos	350.00–400.00
	#2	Same, amethyst	300.00–350.00
	#3	Thermos	12.50– 15.00
	#4,	Ice box water bottle	12.50– 15.00
Row 2:	#1	Georgian ice bucket	35.00– 40.00
	#2	Ice bucket w/metal drainer	30.00– 35.00
	#3	Pink flared rim ice bucket	45.00– 50.00

Row 2: (Continued)

	#4	Pink elephant ice bucket	20.00– 25.00
	#5	Frosted and striped ice bucket	20.00– 25.00
Row 3:	#1	Metallic finish ice bucket	12.50– 15.00
	#2	Cambridge cobalt blue ice bucket	100.00–125.00
	#3,5	Hocking Royal Ruby ribbed or plain water w/lid, ea.	75.00– 85.00
	#4	Black amethyst ice bucket	45.00– 50.00

Ice Buckets
Page 106

Row 1:	#1	Jeannette "Hex Optic" w/reamer top, green	40.00–45.00
	#2	Van Deman "Black Forest," pink	60.00–65.00
	#3	Fostoria "Polar Bear"	30.00–35.00
	#4	McKee, green	20.00–25.00
Row 2:	#1	Fostoria "Swirl," blue	25.00–30.00
	#2	Fostoria "Colony"	60.00–65.00
	#3	Cambridge etched grapes	35.00–40.00
	#4	Fostoria, yellow	30.00–35.00
Row 3:	#1	Fostoria, pink	25.00–30.00
	#2	Fenton, jade	35.00–40.00
	#3	Same, black	40.00–50.00
	#4	Pink w/etched flower & square bottom	25.00–30.00

Row 4:	#1	Cambridge, "Decagon," amethyst	35.00–40.00
	#2	Same, amber	30.00–35.00
	#3	Cambridge, green	25.00–30.00
	#4	Cambridge, #731 or "Rosalie", blue	55.00–65.00
Row 5:	#1	Hocking "Frigidaire Ice Server"	10.00–12.50
	#2	Hocking, "Ring"	12.00–15.00
	#3	Paden City (?) pink	22.00–25.00
	#4	Crystal, Made in U.S.A. (English, other languages on side)	10.00–12.00

Page 107

Row 1:	#1	Fry w/lid, pink	175.00–200.00
	#2	Same, green	200.00–225.00
	#3	Fenton, w/lid, yellow	115.00–135.00
	#4	Fenton, w/lid, jade	75.00– 85.00
Row 2:	#1	Cambridge "Mt. Vernon," red	80.00– 90.00
	#2	Fenton, w/lid, green	55.00– 60.00
	#3	Fenton "Plymouth," red	50.00– 60.00
	#4	Green w/metal lid	20.00– 25.00
Row 3:	#1	Pink "Diamond"	25.00– 27.50
	#2	Green "Zig-Zag"	22.50– 25.00
	#3	Green	18.00– 20.00

Row 3: (Continued)

	#4	Paden City "Party Line" w/etched flowers, pink	25.00– 30.00
Row 4:	#1	Paden City "Party Line," pink	25.00– 30.00
	#2	Same, amber	25.00– 27.50
	#3, 4	Paden City "Cupid," green or pink	125.00–135.00
Row 5:	#1	Paden City "Cupid" ice tub, pink	135.00–150.00
	#2, 3	Paden City "Party Line" ice tub, ea.	25.00– 30.00
	#4	Green ice tub	16.00– 18.00

KNIVES and LADLES

Knife prices have now stabilized. Most of the "comparable" colors are selling in the same price range. All the rarer knives are commanding higher prices!

Boxes add $3.00–5.00 to the price if in excellent condition. Boxes are placed near the knife found in that box. The box on the right in Row 1 of Page 109 says "New York World's Fair."

Page 111 ends the knives and starts the ladle section.

Some knives are priced and not shown.

Page 109		Pink (lt/dk)	Blue	Crystal	Green
Row 1:	#1-3 3 Star, 8½"	25.00– 28.00	28.00– 30.00	8.00–10.00	
	#4-6 3 Star, 9¼"	25.00– 28.00	28.00– 30.00	8.00–10.00	
Row 2:	#1, 2 3 Leaf Dur-X, 8½"	25.00– 28.00	28.00– 30.00	8.00–10.00	25.00– 28.00
	#3, 4 3 Leaf, Dur-X, 9¼"	25.00– 28.00		10.00–12.00	
	#5 Same, (light amber)	125.00–150.00			
	#6-8 5 Leaf, Dur-X, 8½"		17.00– 20.00	10.00–12.00	18.00– 20.00

		Pink (lt/dk)	Amber	Crystal	Green
Row 3:	#1, 2 Rose spray, 8½"	*150.00–175.00	175.00–200.00	50.00–75.00	*150.00–175.00
	#3 Plain handle, 8½"			12.00–15.00	30.00– 35.00
	#4-6 Plain handle, 9¼"	30.00– 35.00			30.00– 35.00
	#7 Same, (pinkish/amber)	60.00– 75.00			

Page 110		Pink (lt/dk)	Amber	Crystal	Green
Row 1:	#1-3 Block, 8¼"	30.00– 35.00		12.00– 15.00	22.50– 37.50
	#4-8 AER-FLO, 7½"	60.00– 70.00	125.00–150.00	30.00– 40.00	60.00– 70.00
	#9 Same, (Forest Green)	150.00–175.00			
Row 2:	#1-3 Steel-ite	80.00– 90.00		35.00– 45.00	65.00– 75.00
	#4 Stonex, 8¼", (white)	150.00–175.00			
	#5-8 Same, light or dark		150.00–175.00		50.00– 60.00
Row 3:	#1 Candlewick, 8½"			200.00–250.00	
	#2 Dagger, 9¼"			75.00– 85.00	
	#3 Westmoreland, Thumb-guard, 9¼"			100.00–115.00	
	#4 Same, Flowers			20.00– 25.00	*175.00–200.00
	#5 Same, minature (sample?)			125.00–150.00	
	#6-8 Buffalo Knife (B.K.Co.), 9¼"			15.00– 18.00	35.00– 40.00

Page 111 Knives top to bottom upper left picture.

#1	Pinwheel	8.00– 10.00
#2,3	Plain	12.00– 15.00
#4-8	Colored handles/blades, ea.	20.00– 25.00

Ladles

Upper Right:

#1	White	30.00– 35.00
#2	"Radiance," blue	135.00–150.00
#3	White, Imperial	40.00– 45.00

Lower Left:

| #1 | Crystal | 25.00– 30.00 |

Lower Left: (Continued)

#2	Black	75.00– 85.00
#3	Crystal	25.00– 30.00
#4	Amber	25.00– 35.00

Lower Right:

#1	Duncan, "Caribbean"	40.00– 45.00
#2	Same, "Hobnail"	25.00– 30.00
#3, 4	Red handled	40.00– 50.00

*Not Shown

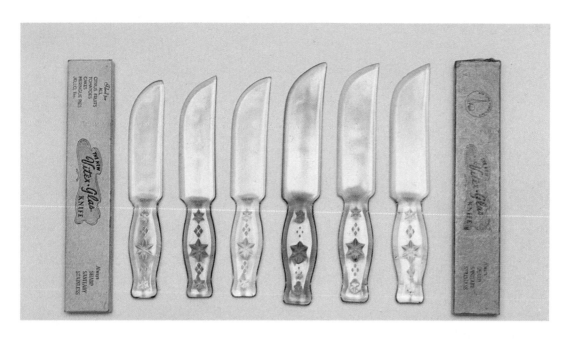

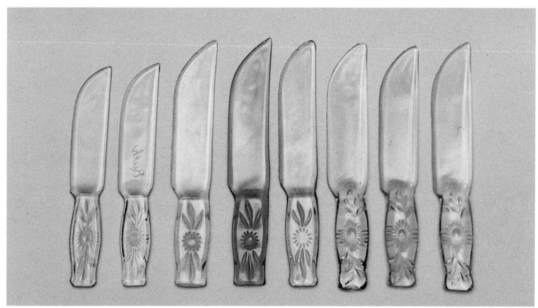

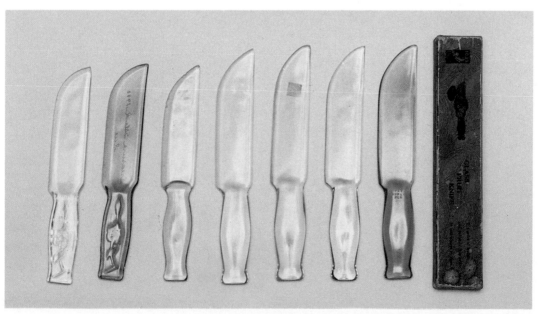

109

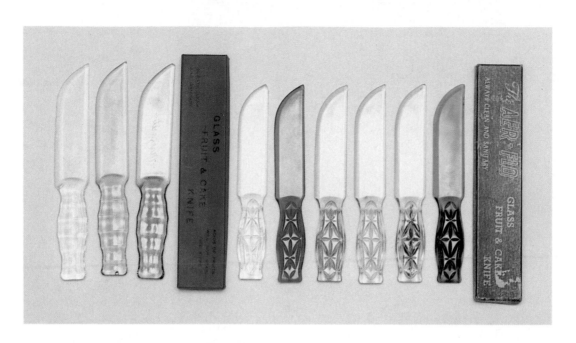

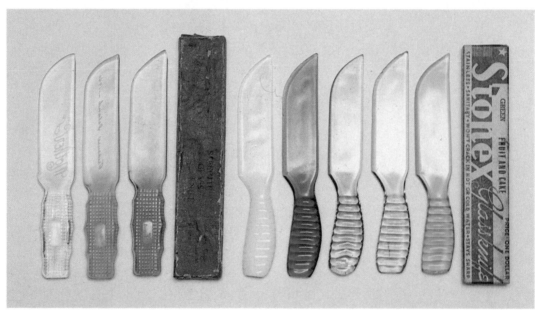

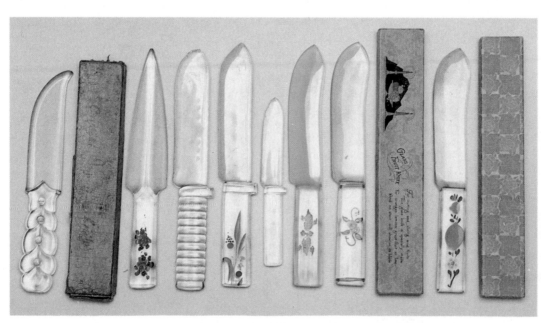

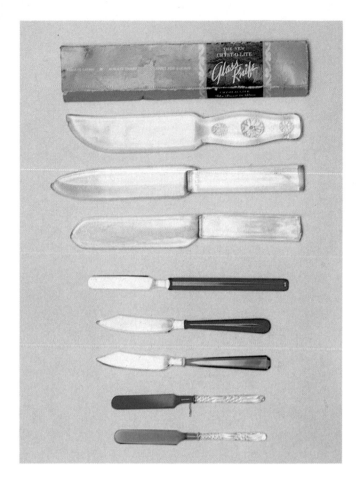

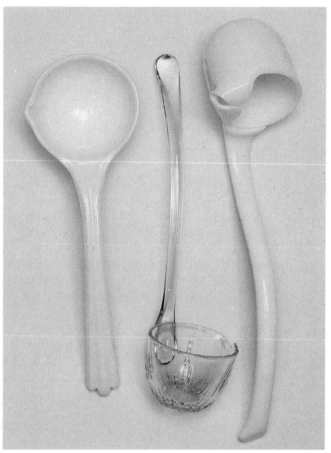

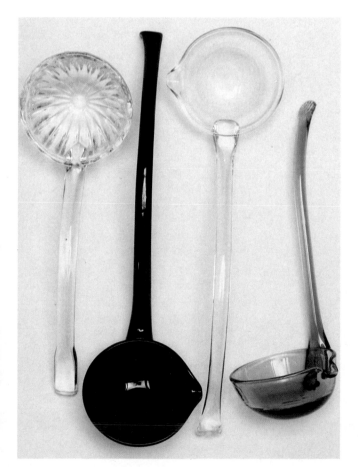

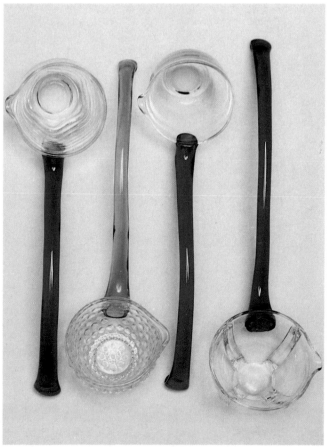

LADLES

Heisey, Fostoria, and Cambridge ladles are the most in demand, although other companies' ladles are collected. An abundance of black ladles with a dwindling demand for them has caused the price of those to plunge.

Page 113

Row 1: #1	Duncan, "Festive"	18.00–20.00
#2, 4	Pink	10.00–12.00
#3, 5	Blue	15.00–18.00
Row 2: #1	Cambridge, pink	18.00–20.00
#2, 3	Same, green	18.00–20.00
#4	Same, Forest Green	20.00–22.00
#5	Same, Moonlight blue	35.00–40.00
#6	Same, amber	12.00–15.00
Column 1:		
#1, 2	Green or yellow	10.00–12.00
#3	Blue, criss crossing design	14.00–16.00
#4, 5	Same, green or yellow	12.00–15.00
Column 2:		
#1	Fostoria, crystal	8.00–10.00
#2	Pink	25.00–30.00

Column 2: (Continued)		
#3, 4	Same, yellow, amber, or *green	20.00–22.50
#5	Same, light blue	35.00–40.00
#6	Same, cobalt blue	35.00–40.00
Column 3:		
#1	Cambridge, blue	22.00–25.00
#2-4	Same, green	10.00–12.00
#5	Same, crystal	5.00– 6.00
Column 4:		
#1	Cambridge, amberina	35.00–40.00
#2	Same, Ivory	20.00–25.00
#3	Same, Primrose	25.00–30.00
#4	Same, Azurite	35.00–40.00
#5	Ebony	20.00–25.00

Page 114

Row 1: #1	Crystal, side spout	10.00–12.00
#2-4	Candlewick, ea.	5.00– 6.00
#5	Higbee, signed bee in bottom	20.00–25.00
Row 2: #1-4	Crystal, unusual shapes, ea.	5.00– 6.50
Column 1 & 2: **All ladles have rounded bottoms.**		
#1 & 4-6	Crystal, plain & etched	3.00– 4.50
#2	Green	10.00–12.00
#3	Black	20.00–25.00
#7	Amethyst	22.00–25.00
Column 2:		
#1, 2 & 4	"Clambroth" green or blue	18.00–20.00
#3	Cobalt blue	25.00–30.00

Column 2: (Continued)		
#5, 6	Pink or amber	10.00–12.00
#7	Black	20.00–25.00
Column 3: **All ladles have wedge shaped handles.**		
#1 & 10	White	6.00– 7.50
#2	Black	20.00–25.00
#3, 4 & 8	Blue, ea.	10.00–12.00
#5	Crystal	3.00– 4.00
#6, 7 & 9	Yellow, pink or green	8.00–10.00
Column 4: **All ladles have rounded handles.**		
#1, 8	Forest green, light blue	10.00–12.00
#2, 5 & 10	Crystal, ea.	3.00– 4.00
#3, 4 & 6	Pink or green	8.00–10.00
#7	Amber	5.00– 6.00
#9	Black	20.00–25.00

Page 115

Row 1: #1-3	All iridized carnival colors	25.00–30.00
Row 2: #1,2	Heisey, Flamingo, ea.	25.00–30.00
#3,4	Same, Hawthorne	30.00–35.00
#5	Same, Moongleam	30.00–35.00
Columns 1 & 2: **All ladles have flat bottoms.**		
Column 1:		
#1, 5	Flashed or amber	8.00–10.00
#2, 4, 6, 7	Yellow, green or pink	10.00–12.00
#3	Blue	15.00–18.00
#8	Cobalt blue, etched	28.00–32.00
Column 2:		
#1	Cobalt blue	25.00–30.00
#2	Amethyst	20.00–22.00

Column 2: (Continued)		
#3	Amber	5.00– 8.00
#4, 6	Frosted blue or vaseline	18.00–20.00
#5	Crystal	3.00– 4.00
Column 3: **All ladle knobs end in triangle shape.**		
#1	Amber	5.00– 8.00
#2	Green	10.00–12.00
#3, 5	Amethyst or vaseline	20.00–25.00
#4	Red	30.00–35.00
Column 4: **All ladle knobs end in straight line.**		
#1	Red	30.00–35.00
#2, 4	Frosted & vaseline	20.00–25.00
#3, 6	Flashed or amber	5.00– 8.00
#5	Green	10.00–12.00

*Not Shown

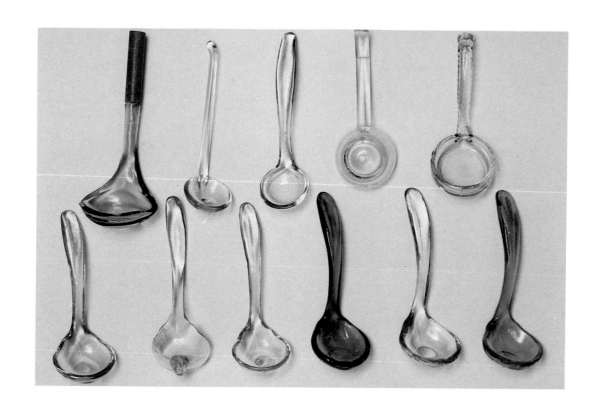

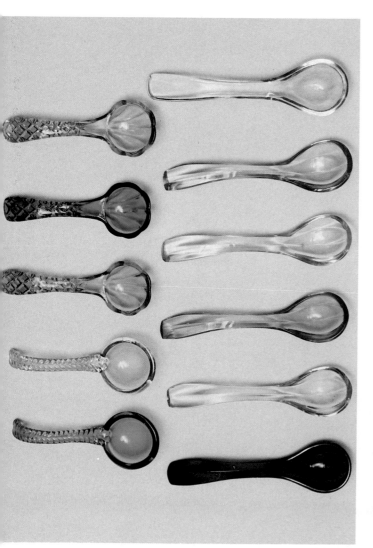

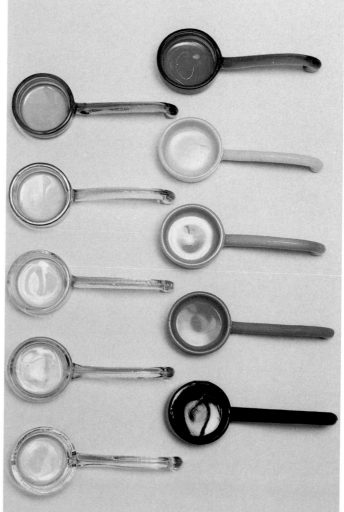

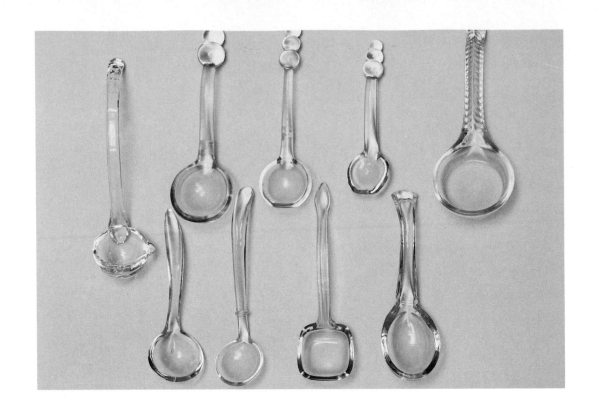

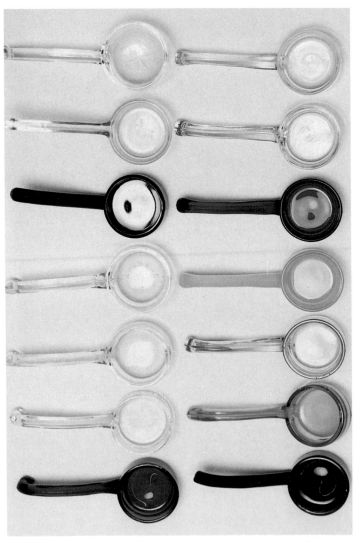

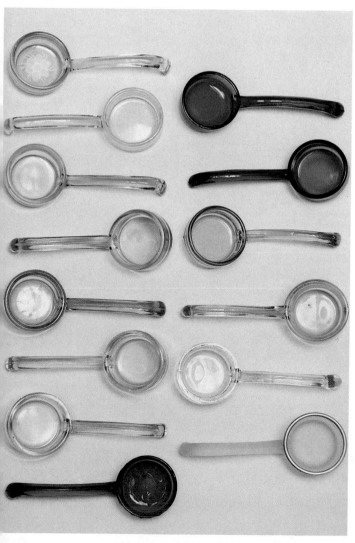

MEASURING CUPS, Advertising & Pattern Glass

Advertising measuring cup prices vary greatly. Dealers who specialize in advertising items seem to value these cups more highly than do measuring cup collectors. Many advertising dealers feel that any cup, including the later Fire King cups with ads, are worth at least $20.00. Some are, but not all! Only two people can decide the price – the buyer and the seller.

There are not many pattern glass measuring cups on the market, but those with lids are harder to find. Lids are interchangeable on many of these cups.

Row 1: #1, 4, 5	Westmoreland w/measure lid (most have advertising in base such as "Finley Acker & Co.," highest grade at lowest cost		75.00– 85.00
	w/o measure lid		35.00– 40.00
#2, 3	Measurements below spout; w/o measure lid $60.00–65.00; w/lid		90.00–100.00
Row 2: #1-4	All Westmoreland w/ads, ea.		20.00– 25.00
	"USE SILAS PIERCE PURE SPICE"		
	"USE SHEPARD'S DRAWING ROOM TEA"		
	"USE S.S.SLEEPER'S, Best of all Spices"		
	"USE GILLESPIE'S ORIENTAL FLOUR"		
#5	"ARCADE MFG. & CO., Freeport, Ill"		20.00– 25.00
Row 3: #1	"SELLER'S," Pat. Dec. 8, 1925		25.00– 30.00
#2	"J W POFF & SONS," Wrightsville, Pa.		20.00– 25.00
#3	"NAPANEE" Dutch Kitchen Cabinet, world's finest kitchen cabinets, Coppes Bros. & Zook, Napanee, IN		20.00– 30.00
#4	"PICKERINGS," Your credit is good, complete home furnishings, 10th & Penn, Pittsburgh		20.00– 30.00
#5	"OWENS & CO."		20.00– 30.00
Row 4: #1	"SILVERS," Brooklyn, Trademark (picture Brooklyn Bridge)		20.00– 30.00
#2	"SAGINAW MILLING CO."		20.00– 30.00
#3	"BUNKER HILL COFFEE"		20.00– 30.00
#4	"CLOVERDALE" quality (4 leaf clover in red)		20.00– 30.00
#5	"CAPITAL B BAND" Handy Cup Measure		25.00– 30.00
Row 5: #1	"TIPPE CANOE," Kitchen Cabinets, none better		20.00– 30.00
#2	"KEYSTONE FURN. CO.," The store that charges less, W King St., Lancaster, Pa.		20.00– 25.00
#3	"HEALTH CLUB" Baking Powder for Success in every baking		20.00– 30.00
#4	"STICKNEY & POOR" Boston Spice Co.		20.00– 30.00
#5	"STICKNEY & POOR" Spice Co.		20.00– 30.00
Row 6: #1	"SCOUT CABIN"		20.00– 25.00
#2	"BROWN EKBERG" Golden Rule Store		20.00– 30.00
#3	"ARMOUR," Use Armour's extract of beef		20.00– 25.00
#4	"FLUFFO," "Be sure of success, use Fluffo shortening & salad oil"		20.00– 25.00
#5	"CREAM DOVE" Brand Peanut Butter Salad Dressing, Cream Dove Mfg. in Binghamton, NY		20.00– 30.00

MEASURING CUPS, Jeannette, McKee, Federal, Hazel Atlas, Anchor Hocking, etc.

See Reproduction Section pages 236-237 for items with asterisk.

Page 119

Rows 1-3: **Jeannette Sets** except *Row 3:* Green $25.00–28.00; Pink $25.00–28.00

	Ultra-marine	Pink	Crystal	Delphite	Jadite
1 cup	50.00– 55.00	45.00– 50.00	30.00– 35.00	45.00– 50.00	20.00–22.00
½ cup	40.00– 45.00	40.00– 45.00	25.00– 30.00	40.00– 45.00	18.00–20.00
⅓ cup	35.00– 40.00	30.00– 35.00	20.00– 25.00	35.00– 40.00	12.00–15.00
¼ cup	25.00– 30.00	25.00– 30.00	15.00– 20.00	30.00– 35.00	8.00–10.00
Set	150.00–170.00	140.00–160.00	90.00–110.00	150.00–170.00	58.00–67.00

Row 4:
- #1 McKee unembossed Glasbake, stippled bottom — 18.00–20.00
- #2 McKee Glasbake, fired-on red — 25.00–30.00
- #3 Glasbake, embossed — 18.00–20.00
- #4 Same, white — 45.00–50.00
- #5 Same, white w/red trim — 45.00–50.00

Row 5:
- #1, 2 Same, handle variations — 12.00–15.00
- #3 Radnt, 2 spout — 60.00–70.00
- #4 Glasbake (A.J. Novite & Sons; Charleston, 3 S.C.) — 15.00–20.00

Row 6:

Chalaine Blue	Black	Seville Yellow	Jadite	Crystal	Caramel
700.00–800.00	700.00–800.00	175.00–195.00	160.00–175.00	55.00–65.00	500.00–600.00

Page 120

Row 1:
- #1 Federal grn., w/o hdl., 3 spt. — 25.00–28.00
- #2 Same, crystal — 15.00–18.00
- #3 Same, amber — 35.00–38.00
- #4 Same, 3 spout, handle ad: "Easy Combomatic Washer/Dryer" — 20.00–22.50
- #5 Same, pink — 55.00–60.00
- #6 Same, amber — 35.00–38.00

Row 2:
- #1, 3 Same, solid hdl, 1 or 3 spt. — 35.00–40.00
- #2 Same, crystal — 20.00–22.50
- #4 Fry, 3 spout — 65.00–75.00
- #5 Same, 1 spout — 50.00–60.00

Row 3:
- #1-3 Hazel Atlas 3 spt white/trim — 55.00–65.00
- #4 Same, flashed green — 32.00–35.00
- #5, 6 Same, white or flashed red — 35.00–40.00

Row 4:
- #1, 2 Hazel Atlas 1 or 3 spout, green — 20.00–25.00
- #3, 4 Same, pink, no embossing — 30.00–35.00
- #5 Same, crystal — 12.00–15.00

Row 5:
- #1 Hazel Atlas 3 spout, yellow — 225.00–250.00
- #2 Same, cobalt blue — *350.00–400.00
- #3 Green, HA embosssed — 20.00–25.00
- #4 Kellogg's embossed, pink — *25.00–30.00
- #5 Kellogg's embossed, green — *20.00–25.00

Row 6:
- #1 Cambridge, crystal — 20.00–25.00
- #2 Heisey, crystal — 225.00–250.00
- #3, 4 Foreign, ea. — 18.00–20.00
- #5 Blue foreign, EJKRONT (measures tea, coffee, wine) — 45.00–50.00
- #6 Cobalt blue, foreign "SEPDELEN" — 75.00–85.00

Page 121

Row 1:
- #1 Fire King, blue 3 spout — 18.00–20.00
- #2 Fire King, blue 1 spout — 15.00–18.00
- #3 Fire King, crystal w/red — 3.00–5.00
- #4 Gr. emb "Urban's Liberty Flour" — 65.00–75.00
- #5 Pyrex, 2 spout — 22.00–25.00
- #6 Pyrex, 1 spout — 8.00–10.00

Row 2:
- #1, 2 Green "Clambroth," ea. — 150.00–175.00
- #3-5 Hocking green, ea. — 25.00–28.00
- #6 Hocking crystal — 12.00–15.00

Row 3:
- #1 Gr. slick hdl., dry measure "Sellers" — 50.00–60.00
- #2 Same, "E.E. Hamm," Hanover, Pa. — 25.00–28.00
- #3, 5 U.S. Glass slick, hdl., 2 spout, ea. — 35.00–40.00
- #4 Same, green, 1 spout — 30.00–35.00
- #6 Crystal, dry measure — 12.00–15.00

Row 4:
- #1 U.S. Glass pink, 1 spout — 50.00–60.00
- #2, 3 U.S. Glass, green 1 or 3 spout — 30.00–35.00

Row 4: (Continued)
- #4 Spoon measure — 4.00–5.00
- #5 U.S. Glass, dry measure, white — 175.00–200.00
- #6 Paden City, green — 100.00–125.00

Row 5:
- #1 Green 3 spout — 75.00–85.00
- #2 Crystal, oval — 15.00–20.00
- #3 Same, green — 40.00–50.00
- #4 Tufglas — 85.00–100.00
- #5, 6 Crystal, (rnd bot) or "Ideal" measure — 25.00–30.00

Row 6:
- #1 Green, 1 spout — 75.00–85.00
- #2, 4, 5 Crystal, 1 spt, or rectangular, ea. — 14.00–16.00
- #3 Amber, 1 spout — 225.00–250.00
- #6 Amber — 25.00–30.00
- #7, 8 Crystal "Root Tea"/"My Pet Milk" — 20.00–25.00

MEASURING CUPS, Rare and Unusual

There are some difficult to find measuring cups shown here. The footed four cup pitchers in Delphite and "Caramel" are the only ones ever found in those colors. I reiterate from the last book that, "Pricing unique pieces is at best, a guess."

It is difficult to obtain an accurate price on items that have not been sold in years. For example, a Chalaine blue four cup measure without handles was bought for $100.00 in 1980. One of these just sold for $1500.00 in Colorado. Is the only other one known worth the same – or more? How many collectors are willing to pay that much for the privilege of owning a Chalaine blue four cup measure?

Row 1:	#1	Chalaine Blue, 4 cup, no handle	1,250.00–1,500.00
	#2	Same, Seville yellow	350.00– 400.00
	#3	Same, Jadite green	300.00– 350.00
	#4	Same, crystal	75.00– 85.00
	#5	Tufglas, 4 cup	55.00– 65.00
Row 2:	#1	Seville yellow, 4 cup, ftd. w/hdl	115.00– 130.00
	#2	Same, Chalaine blue	300.00– 400.00
	#3	Same, Jadite	25.00– 30.00
	#4	Same, Custard	30.00– 35.00
Row 3:	#1	Cambridge dry measure, green	225.00– 250.00
	#2	Cambridge, 1 spout, 1 cup, pink	200.00– 225.00
	#3	Same, green	200.00– 225.00
	#4	U.S. Glass, 2 cup, pink	150.00– 175.00
Row 4:	#1	McKee, 4 cup, Caramel	500.00– 600.00
	#2	Same, Delphite	450.00– 500.00
	#3	Unknown, green, 2 cups = 1 pt. & 20 oz. = 1 pt. on side	125.00– 150.00

MEASURING CUP

1C778—8 oz., 3 in. high, heavy crystal, well finished, graduated for cups. 4 doz. in carton, 48 lbs.............**Doz 48c**

GLASS MEASURING CUPS

No. 3   **No. 2**

No. 3—Half Pint Glass Measuring Cup. Packed 2 dozen to carton.
Per dozen $1.56
No. 2—Half Pint Glass Measuring Cup. Packed 2 dozen to carton.
Per dozen $2.20

MEASURING CUPS

Emerald Green

1C2193 — 8 oz., 3 in. high, clear crystal, lipped, graduated for ounces and pints. 2 doz. in carton, 30 lbs.....**Doz 78c**

1C779—8 oz., 3½ in. high, substantial pressed **emerald green** glass, graduated for ounces and cups. 2 doz. in carton, 25 lbs.   **Doz 85c**

1C2183—2 styles, plain and side lip, 8 oz., 3¼ in. high, clear crystal, graduated for ounces and cups. Asstd. 3 doz. in carton. **Doz 79c**

MEASURING CUPS CO-734 —. 2 doz in carton, 18 lbs
Doz 78c
8 oz., 3⅝ in., pressed cup and ounce graduated.

MEASURING PITCHERS, 2 Cups or More

Nearly all the measuring pitchers are bought by reamer collectors looking for bottoms to go with their reamer tops or hoping to find tops to the pitcher later. There are some rarities in these pitchers. Take note of the green one in Row 2 on page 127. It is probably the most desirable on these three pages.

There are more measuring cup collectors than there are measuring pitcher collectors. Owning decorated McKee two cup pitchers alone could fill several shelves in your china cabinet! Just take a look at the top three rows on Page 125. Considering that each of those designs could come on white or Custard as well as all the different colors gives an idea how many reamer tops you would need to complete these sets. **See Reproduction Section pages 236 – 237 for items marked with asterisk (*).**

Page 125

Rows 1-4 **All McKee 2 Cup**

Row 1:	#1, 2	"Diamond Check," red or black	25.00–30.00
	#3	Floral decal	25.00–30.00
	#4, 5	Green or red "Dots" on white	25.00–28.00
Row 2:	#1-3	Floral, black or red bows, ea.	22.00–25.00
	#4, 5	"Ships"	27.00–30.00
Row 3:	#1, 2	Black or orange "Dots" on custard	35.00–38.00
	#3	Custard w/red trim	18.00–20.00
	#4	Custard	15.00–18.00
	#5	Seville yellow	30.00–35.00
Row 4:	#1	Jadite	12.00–15.00
	#2	Delphite	75.00–85.00

Row 4:	(Continued)		
	#3	Fired-on green	12.00–15.00
	#4	Glasbake, crystal	20.00–22.00
Row 5:	#1, 2	U.S.Glass, slick handle, pink or green	40.00–45.00
	#3	Same, crystal	18.00–20.00
	#4	Iridized carnival	35.00–45.00
	#5	Crystal	8.00–10.00
Row 6:	**All Jeannette 2 Cup (Sunflower in bottom)**		
	#1	Green transparent	75.00–85.00
	#2	Jadite, dark	45.00–450.00
	#3	Jadite, light	15.00–18.00
	#4	Delphite	60.00–70.00

Page 126

Row 1:	#1	Hocking, 2 cup, green	15.00– 20.00
	#2	Same, ribbed, green	40.00– 45.00
	#3	Same, crystal	15.00– 20.00
	#4	Same, pink	35.00– 40.00
Row 2:	#1	Green "Clambroth"	100.00–125.00
	#2	Vitrock white w/lid	30.00– 40.00
	#3	Fire-King, 16 oz., 2 spout, blue	22.50– 25.00
		Same, crystal embossed "Diamond Crystal Shaker Salt"	20.00– 25.00
	#4	"Grandma's Old Time Measure," made in Italy, 1971	15.00– 18.00
Row 3:	#1	Embossed "A & J"	10.00– 12.00
	Hazel Atlas (Measuring & Mixing in base)		
	#2	Fired-on red	35.00– 40.00

Row 3:	(Continued)		
	#3, 4	White w/decorated colored bands	20.00– 25.00
Row 4:	#1, 3 & 4	White w/Dots	30.00– 35.00
	#2	Green w/white Dots	40.00– 45.00
	#5	Black floral decal	30.00– 35.00
Row 5:	#1	Iridized	85.00–100.00
	#2	Transparent green	20.00– 25.00
	#3	Crystal	8.00– 10.00
	#4	Crystal, "Spry"	12.50– 15.00
Row 6:	#1	Cobalt blue	*150.00–175.00
	#2	Pink, light	*40.00– 50.00
	#3	Pink, dark	*75.00– 90.00
	#4	Yellow	200.00–225.00

Page 127

Row 1:	#1	"Ocean Mills," Montreal, Canada (Man holding box of Chinese starch), 2½ pt.	60.00– 75.00
	#2	"Davis Baking Powder," ½ gal.	60.00– 75.00
	#3	½ gal.	40.00– 50.00
Row 2:	#1	1 qt.	25.00– 35.00
	#2	1 qt., green	600.00–650.00
	#3	Cambridge, 1 qt., measure top	85.00–100.00
	#4	Baby formula, 20 oz., (foreign) Estans Materna	20.00– 25.00
Row 3:	#1	Umpire Glass Co., Pittsburgh, 1 qt.	20.00– 25.00

Row 3:	(Continued)		
	#2	Silvers Brooklyn Trademark, 1 qt.	20.00– 25.00
	#3	Sanitary Bess Mixer (embossed "4" inside a large "1")	175.00–200.00
	#4	Lighting Dasher Egg Beater Co., 1 pt.	18.00– 20.00
	#5	Hazel Atlas 4 cup crystal	12.00– 15.00
Row 4:	#1, 2	Hazel Atlas frosted green & white w/red trim, ea.	*18.00– 20.00
	#3, 4	Hazel Atlas A&J green or white w/black trim, ea.	20.00– 25.00

MECHANICAL ATTACHMENTS

Shown on the right below and in the middle of Row 3 on page 129 are two different "Cold Water Coffee Extractors." Neither of these were ever used so they may have been a great idea that wasn't popular. Instructions for use are shown on page 130. Additionally, instructions for the "Economy Dispenser" pictured below on the left are shown on page 131.

Page 128

Row 1:

#1	Filtron cold water coffee extractor		125.00–150.00
#2	Economy dispenser		50.00– 60.00

Page 129

Row 1:

#1	Mayonnaise maker		12.50– 15.00
#2	Sugar shaker (one tsp. measure top)		35.00– 40.00
#3	Honey or other liquid dispenser		15.00– 17.50
#4	Syrup dispenser		12.50– 15.00
#5	"Vidrio" electric mixer w/green base		50.00– 60.00

Row 2:

#1	Mixer		8.00– 10.00
#2	Food chopper		10.00– 12.00
#3	Mixer		8.00– 10.00
#4	Mixer, bands at 4-8-12 oz. marks		8.00– 10.00
#5	Electric beater		20.00– 25.00

Row 3:

#1	Mixer		8.00– 10.00
#2	Measure for CoffeeX coffee extractor		10.00– 12.50
#3	CoffeeX cold water coffee extractor		125.00–150.00
#4	Green butter churn		250.00–285.00

PARTS LIST

OPERATING INSTRUCTIONS

Helmco-Lacy

FILTRON

COLD WATER COFFEE EXTRACTOR

It's as simple as A-B-C to operate — it requires less than two minutes to assemble your new Filtron if you follow the simple instructions. Then with Filtron extract always in your refrigerator you will have the most delicious cup of coffee you ever tasted — ready at an instant's notice. Follow these instructions and your Filtron will give you long, treasured service.

CARE OF NEW UNIT

Rinse the parts of your new Filtron thoroughly with cold drinking water—*do not use soap*—to remove the dust. Nothing else is necessary before starting the following simple instructions.

INSTRUCTIONS FOR OPERATING

- Fill water bowl with 60 oz. of clear, cold drinking water.
- Flush cold drinking water through plastic filter.
- Screw filter on water bowl so it cushions gently against rubber ring. (Use slight pressure of fingers only.)
- Insert rubber stopper in coffee bowl from **bottom**.
- Saturate felt pad **thoroughly**, cup slightly, and place in position, **tab up**.

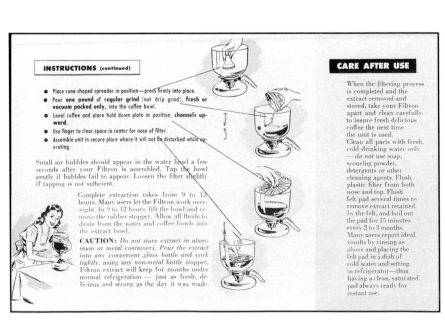

INSTRUCTIONS (continued)

- Place cone shaped spreader in position—press firmly into place.
- Pour **one pound of regular grind** (not drip grind), **fresh or vacuum packed only**, into the coffee bowl.
- Level coffee and place hold down plate in position, **channels upward**.
- Use finger to clear space in center for nose of filter.
- Assemble unit in secure place where it will not be disturbed while operating.

Small air bubbles should appear in the water bowl a few seconds after your Filtron is assembled. Tap the bowl gently if bubbles fail to appear. Loosen the filter slightly if tapping is not sufficient.

Complete extraction takes from 9 to 12 hours. Many users let the Filtron work overnight. In 9 to 12 hours, lift the bowl and remove the rubber stopper. Allow all fluids to drain from the water and coffee bowls into the extract bowl.

CAUTION: *Do not store extract in aluminum or metal containers. Pour the extract into any convenient glass bottle and cork tightly, using any non-metal bottle stopper.* Filtron extract will keep for months under normal refrigeration — just as fresh, delicious and strong as the day it was made.

CARE AFTER USE

When the filtering process is completed and the extract removed and stored, take your Filtron apart and clean carefully to insure fresh delicious coffee the next time the unit is used. Clean all parts with fresh, cold drinking water only — *do not* use soap, scouring powder, detergents or other cleaning agents. Flush plastic filter from both nose and top. Flush felt pad several times to remove extract retained by the felt, and boil out the pad for 15 minutes every 2 to 3 months. Many users report ideal results by rinsing as above and placing the felt pad in a dish of cold water and setting in refrigerator—thus having a clean, saturated pad always ready for instant use.

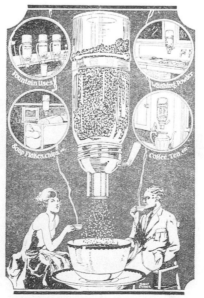

131

MECHANICAL ATTACHMENTS (Continued)

I recently received a letter from a reader requesting instructions on how to work the two ice cream makers. These sanitary freezers, as they were called, are shown in the middle of Row 1 on page 133 and on the end of Row 1 on page 134. The instructions for operating the one on page 133 were in it, but I did not take them out to see how it was done. I suspect they were the "Ronco" of the radio age. You probably stir, put in ice box, stir later and put back in ice box, hoping not to blow up the glass container.

These accessory items make up some of the more unusual items in Kitchenware collecting. For those who collect colors, there are mechanical or hand beaters in almost every color. If you collect Fire King, there is a popcorn maker.

A one quart ice cream maker is shown at the bottom of page 134. An ice cube breaker is attached right beside it. I thought this was a great idea, but it was the first I had seen; so it may not have been too popular! I do know how to make this one work! I have done that chore! This is quite heavy; we had to triple the glass shelves to hold the mixer and the ice cream maker.

Page 133

Row 1:			
#1	"Keystone" beater, Pat. Dec. 1885, North Bros.	60.00– 75.00
#2	Jewel "Beater Mixer" (mfg. by Juergens Bros., Minn., Mn.)	40.00– 45.00
#3	Sanitary glass ice cream freezer (Consolidated Mfg. Co.)	75.00– 90.00
#4	Mixer, 1 qt. capacity	8.00– 10.00
#5	"Ladd" beater, green or pink (not shown)	30.00– 35.00

Row 2:		
#1	Hydraulic "Niagara" food mixer (attaches to faucet)	30.00– 35.00
#2	Thermos (mercury lined), "Higbee Hot/Cold Sanitary Bottle"	75.00– 85.00

Row 2: (Continued)		
#3	Criss Cross food mixer (baby face on side)	40.00– 50.00
#4	Mixer, bands at 4-8-12 oz. marks, Kamkap, Inc., U.S.A.	8.00– 10.00
#5	Fire-King popcorn popper	35.00– 40.00

Row 3:		
#1	"Vidrio" electric mixer w/ cobalt blue base	110.00–125.00
#2	Same, w/custard slag base	40.00– 45.00
#3	"Chicago Electric" beater w/ Jadite bottom	35.00– 40.00
#4	"Challenge" w/Custard bottom	25.00– 30.00
#5	"Kenmore" electric beater	20.00– 25.00

Page 134

Row 1:		
#1	Delphite beater bowl	60.00– 70.00
#2	Jadite beater bowl	25.00– 30.00
#3	White beater bowl	12.50– 15.00
#4	Iridized beater bowl	30.00– 35.00
#5	Sanitary freezer	60.00– 75.00

Row 2:		
#1	Handy Andy Juice Extractor	30.00– 35.00
#2	Juice extractor	75.00– 85.00
#3	Ser-Mor Juice Extractor Pat.	50.00– 60.00

Row 2: (Continued)		
#4	Vidrio Products Corp. "Gem Squeezer" Cicero, Il.	40.00– 50.00

Row 3:		
#1	Mixer, w/Chalaine bowl	75.00–100.00
#2	"Deluxe Lightning One Quart Ice Cream Maker" w/Lightning Ice Cube Breaker by North Brothers	65.00–100.00

Page 135

Row 1:		
#1	"J. Hutchanson" Trademark S&S Long Island (Mayonnaise)	100.00–125.00
#2	Cobalt beater	75.00–100.00
#3	Ultra-marine beater	50.00– 55.00
#4	Pink beater	30.00– 35.00

Row 2:		
#1	"Bromo-Seltzer" dispenser	135.00–150.00
#2	"Ladd" mixer churn #2	85.00–100.00
#3	Mixer (similar to Keystone)	60.00– 75.00
#4	"Silver & Co." food mixer	20.00– 25.00
#5	"Bordens" Pat. Mar. 30, 1915	18.00– 22.00

135

MISCELLANEOUS and MIXERS

Every time you have a large photography session for a book, there are items that do not go in the categories you are presently working on. Also, there are times that a quantity of harder to find items are available to be photographed when you are not even working on a book at the time. That is how pages 137 and 138 came to be. On page 139 are two complete mixers. The insert in the top of the mixer is impossible to find. Separately, that piece is worth more than the rest of the mixer. The mechanical parts of these mixers are worth very little. Their being glass makes them collectable.

Page 137

Row 1:	#1	Fry covered jug		150.00– 175.00
	#2	Unusual Fry pitcher		100.00– 125.00
	#3	Paden City cobalt blue sugar shaker		600.00– 650.00
Row 2:	#1	Green sugar shaker		150.00– 175.00
	#2	Pink sugar shaker		175.00– 200.00
	#3	Cobalt blue 3 ftd. sugar shaker (New Martinsville)?		750.00– 850.00
	#3,4	Green door knobs, pr.		100.00– 125.00
	#5,6	Cobalt blue door knobs, pr.		150.00– 200.00
Row 3:	#1	"Paramount" napkin holder, black		400.00– 450.00
	#2	Same, pink		375.00– 425.00
	#3	Candlewick knife		200.00– 250.00
Row 4:	#1	Hocking "Mayfair blue" reamer		1250.00–1500.00
	#2	Teal measure cup		175.00– 200.00
	#3	Salad set, cobalt blue		200.00– 250.00

Page 138

Row 1:	#1,5	Hocking batter dispenser		15.00– 20.00
	#2,4	Syrup dispensers to match above		12.50– 15.00
	#3	Pitcher to match #1,2		15.00– 20.00
Row 2:	#1	Red mug		30.00– 35.00
	#2	Crown Tuscan mug		65.00– 75.00
	#3	Crystal McKee "Bottoms Down" mug		135.00–150.00
	#4	"Elsie" sundae		10.00– 12.50
	#5	Striped cocktail shaker		10.00– 12.50
	#6	Cambridge pinch decanter		45.00– 50.00
Row 3:	#1-7	Comic cocktail shaker set "Sweet Ad-aline"		40.00– 45.00
	#8	Tumbler, 8 oz., matches #9		3.00– 4.00
	#9	Cocktail shaker "Gay 90's" scene		10.00– 12.50
	#10	Tumbler, 4 oz., matches #9		3.00– 4.00
	#11	New Martinsville "Prelude" cocktail shaker, 32 oz.		65.00– 75.00

Page 139

Top:	#1	Seville yellow mixer complete		150.00–200.00
	#2	Top bowl only		20.00– 25.00
	#3	Top bowl juicer insert		75.00 100.00
Bottom:	#1	Chalaine Blue mixer		450.00–500.00
	#2	Top bowl only		50.00– 75.00
	#3	Top bowl juicer insert		250.00–300.00

139

MUGS

More mug collectors are beginning to ask for these items at shows than in the past. You can obtain a small collection without much searching, but after the first twenty or so, you will have to work to find additional ones. Many of these mug collectors are not aware that Kitchenware collectors also seek mugs to go along with their glassware.

The Seville and Jadite "Bottoms Down" mugs on Row 4 always create the most interesting comments from non-collectors. A crystal one is pictured later in the book. At mall antique shows, the little old ladies always look embarrassed about picking one up. Not much later, guess who sneaks back to show a friend?

The most expensive mug is the pink Colonial shown in Row 3. This also comes in green, but only three have ever been found in that color!

The last mug on the bottom row is Moondrops. This mug can be found in several colors as well as two sizes.

Note the ad below for a "Beer Set" featuring the mug shown in Row 3: #3. These sets were made by Hocking and today, would fetch $280.00-315.00 as shown with six mugs. That is up somewhat from the $0.95 price of yesteryear.

Row 1: #1	Green root beer	25.00– 30.00
#2	Same pink	22.00– 25.00
#3	Pink frosted root beer	25.00– 30.00
#4	Yellow root beer	30.00– 35.00
#5	Amber	35.00– 40.00
Row 2: #1	Forest Green, Cambridge	40.00– 45.00
#2	Yellow, same	35.00– 40.00
#3	Crystal, Heisey "Old Sandwich" pilsner	20.00– 30.00
#4	Pink, called "Adam's Rib" by collectors	18.00– 20.00
#4	Same, green	20.00– 25.00
Row 3: #1	Colonial, pink, Hocking	450.00–500.00
#2	Black, "Genolite"	30.00– 35.00
#3	Green, pretzel, Hocking	28.00– 30.00
#4	Peacock blue	25.00– 30.00
#5	Forest Green, Cambridge "Mt. Vernon"	30.00– 35.00
Row 4: #1	Green soda fountain type	20.00– 25.00
#2	Same, apple green	20.00– 25.00

Row 4: (Continued)		
#3	Seville yellow, McKee "Bottoms Down"	135.00–150.00
#4	Same, Jadite	135.00–150.00
#5	Green, Imperial "Chesterfield"	22.00– 25.00
#6	Same, amber	20.00– 22.50
Row 5: #1	Red, New Martinsville	22.50– 25.00
#2	Light blue	20.00– 22.00
#3	Red, Cambridge "Tally-Ho"	25.00– 28.00
#4	Green, Hobnail	20.00– 22.00
#5	Green	17.50– 20.00
#6	Amber, applied handle	20.00– 22.50
Row 6: #1	Pink, footed Jeannette	25.00– 28.00
#2	Same, green	22.50– 25.00
#3	Green, Fostoria "Priscilla"	12.50– 15.00
#4	Green	35.00– 40.00
#5	Cobalt, New Martinsville "Moondrops"	30.00– 35.00

NAPKIN HOLDERS

The "Paramount" pink napkin holder shown below sells in the $375.00–425.00 range. This "Paramount" also comes in green and black. You can see a black one on page 137.

The white one shown below says HY-G Napkins on it. It sold for $150.00.

The light blue in Row 2: #3 may be a letter holder; but in any case, it is of foreign manufacture.

Napkin Holders continue to be one of the most difficult kitchenware items to photograph. Most are the same size and shape. Since they are flat, embossed lettering disappears when they are placed in rows. That does not take into consideration the white or black ones. The whites disappear from the photo if you light from the back. The blacks vanish if you light from the front. This is just one of the minor details that we struggle with as we work through our picture taking marathons.

Row 1:	#1	White, NAR-O-FOLD, "Property of trade Nar-O-Fold mark Napkin Company, Chicago, reg. U.S.A.	35.00– 45.00
	#2	Frosted crystal	35.00– 45.00
	#3	Crystal, vertical ribbed	35.00– 45.00
	#4	Black, same as #1	115.00–135.00
Row 2:	#1	Crystal, horizontal ribs, L.E. Smith	37.50– 45.00
	#2	Forest Green	80.00– 85.00
	#3	Light blue, foreign	65.00– 75.00
	#4	White, Paden City "Party Line"	45.00– 50.00
Row 3:	#1	Pink, Paden City "Party Line"	120.00–135.00
	#2	Same, green	100.00–125.00
	#3	Same, black	115.00–135.00

Row 3:	(Continued)		
	#4	Same, crystal	45.00– 50.00
Row 4:	#1	Green "Clambroth," SERV-ALL	150.00–175.00
	#2	Same, opal white	45.00– 55.00
	#3	Same, white	45.00– 55.00
	#4	White, Ft. Howard HANDI-NAP	45.00– 55.00
	#5	White, SLEN-DR-FOLD	50.00– 55.00
Row 5:	#1	White, FAN FOLD, Property of Diana Mfg., Green Bay	65.00– 75.00
	#2	Green, FAN FOLD, no other embossing	100.00–120.00
	#3	Same, Forest green	110.00–125.00
	#4	Green, same as #1	100.00–120.00
	#5	Crystal, same as #2	55.00– 60.00

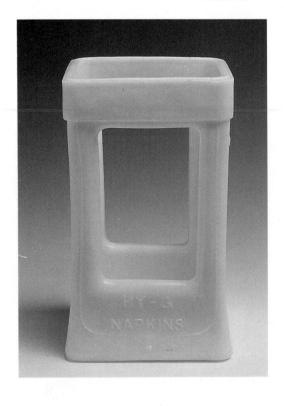 

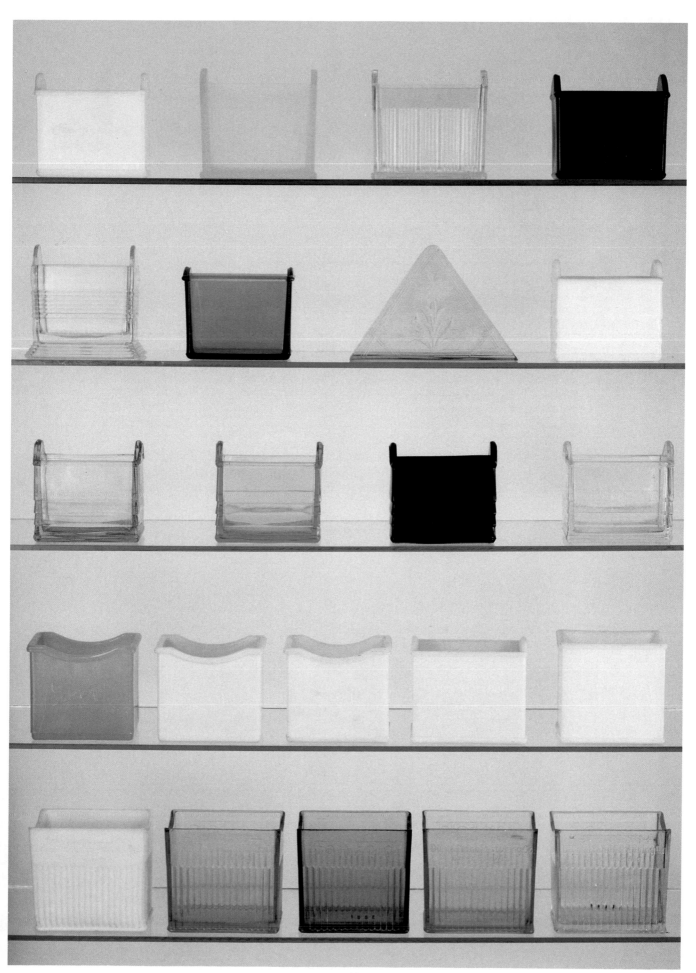

OIL & VINEGAR or FRENCH DRESSING BOTTLES

Fostoria and Cambridge oil and vinegar bottles are in demand by collectors who are looking for the better known etched patterns. While plain or unetched varieties do sell, they do not sell nearly as fast or at as lofty a price. Amber colored bottles are the slowest to sell no matter which company made them or what etching may be on them.

The correct stopper for the pyramid shaped bottle in the bottom row can be seen on page 49. Over the years many bottles had substitute stoppers added. Like lids and cups, many a stopper dropped! Note that colored bottles often have crystal stoppers.

Row 1:	#1	Paden City, green	50.00– 60.00
	#2	Same, pink	50.00– 60.00
	#3	Cambridge, etched pattern, green	75.00– 85.00
	#4	Same, no etching	50.00– 60.00
	#5	Cambridge, amber w/crystal stopper	25.00– 30.00
	#6	Same, w/amber stopper	40.00– 45.00
	#7	Green set (late 1940's)	30.00– 35.00
Row 2:	#1	Cambridge "Rosalie" (#731), pink	100.00–115.00
	#2	Same, green	110.00–125.00
	#3, 5, 7	Cambridge crystal, ea.	18.00– 22.00
	#4	Cambridge w/sterling stopper	45.00– 50.00
	#6	Hawkes, green	75.00– 85.00
Row 3:	#1	Heisey, "Flamingo" pink	65.00– 75.00
	#2	Same, crystal ("Mfg. under license granted by T.G. Hawkes & Co.; Fill w/vinegar to line marked Vinegar, w/oil to line marked Oil, salt & pepper, etc., to taste, shake & you have perfect dressing")	35.00– 45.00
	#3	Heisey "Twist," pink	85.00– 95.00
	#4, 9	Fostoria amber, ea.	35.00– 40.00
	#5	Fostoria w/sterling top	20.00– 22.00
	#6, 7	Fostoria, yellow or green	65.00– 75.00
	#8	Fostoria yellow w/crystal top	45.00– 50.00
Row 4:	#1	Paden City "Party Line," pink	55.00– 65.00
	#2	Unknown "pyramid" style (wrong stopper; see p.43)	45.00– 55.00
	#3	Cambridge set, 3 pc. pink	50.00– 65.00
	#4	Crackle set (possibly Cambridge)	40.00– 50.00
	#5	Yellow	25.00– 30.00
	#6	Cambridge pink	25.00– 30.00
	#7	Amber	25.00– 27.50

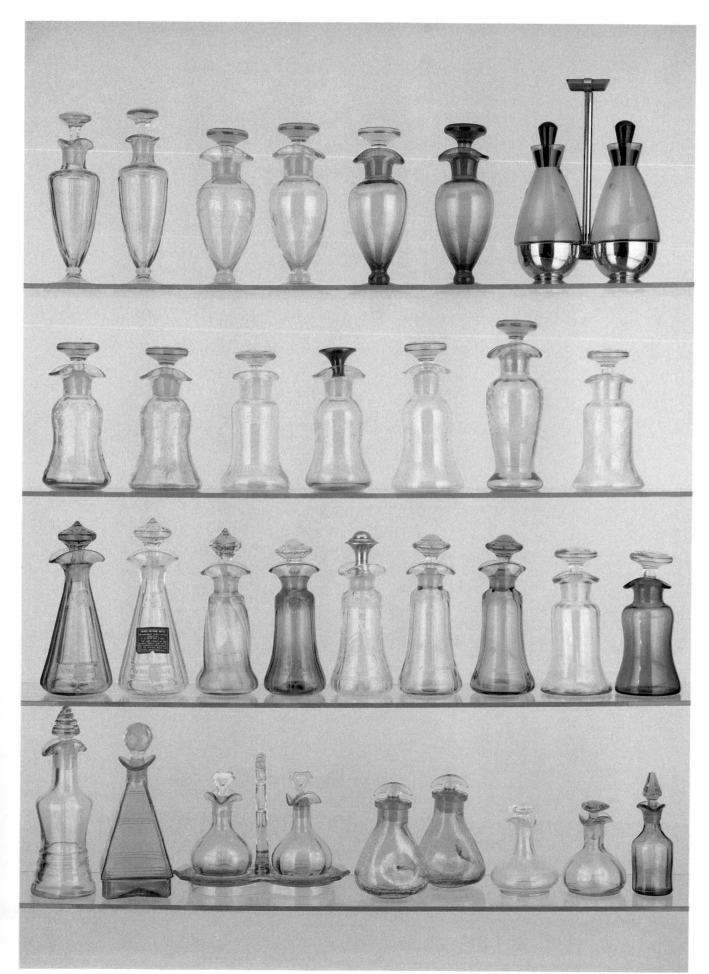

REAMERS, Baby

These two part reamers are twice as difficult to find perfect as the one piece reamers.

The Barnes reamer shown in Row 3 was only the beginning of the repros. Unfortunately, original molds were bought after Westmoreland's demise and used to make some reproductions. The Barnes reamers are all marked with B in a circle. However, Summit Art Glass of Akron, Ohio, is using original molds under a private contract without marking the glass in any way!

Other repros have come from Taiwan. See pages 236 – 237 on reproductions. Items with an asterisk below have been reproduced. To keep abreast of all the reamer news I suggest you join the national reamer club. The address is as follows: National Reamer Collectors Association, c/o Larry Brandstad, 405 Benson Rd. W., Frederic, WI 54837-8945.

Westmoreland Glass Company (Rows 1-3)

Row 1:	#1	Pink, 2 piece	150.00–175.00
	#2	Same, crystal	45.00– 55.00
	#3	Blue (bottom only $90.00-100.00)	200.00–225.00
	#4	Amber, 2 piece	175.00–200.00
	#5	Sun-colored-amethyst (bottom only $40.00-45.00)	80.00– 90.00
	#6	Green, 2 piece	175.00–200.00

Row 2 & 3: **Bottom is worth ⅔ of price except where noted below.**

*Row 2:	#1	Frosted pink	110.00–125.00
	#2	Green (top & bottom about equal in value)	200.00–225.00
	#3	Crystal w/decorations	35.00– 40.00
	#4	Pink (bottom value $20.00-25.00)	125.00–150.00
	#5	Frosted blue bottom only	40.00– 45.00
	#6	Sun-colored-amethyst (SCA)	50.00– 60.00
*Row 3:	#1	Frosted crystal (decorated add $10.00)	45.00– 50.00
	#2	Pink decorated	125.00–140.00
	#3	Blue (bottom value $25.00-30.00)	155.00–175.00
	#4, 5	NEW! RUBINA AND COBALT BLUE MARKED WITH B IN CIRCLE INSIDE CONE OF TOP AND ON BOTTOM OF BASE	

SEE PAGE 235 FOR ADDITIONAL COLORS.

Row 4:	#1	L.E. Smith (top rare), pink	250.00–275.00
	#2	Same, green	250.00–275.00
	#3	Same, crystal (in metal add $5.00)	20.00– 30.00
	#4	Jenkins, green	125.00–150.00
	#5	Same, crystal	30.00– 35.00
	#6	Same, frosted crystal	40.00– 45.00
Row 5:	#1	Unknown, blue (top $200.00)	450.00–450.00
	#2	Unknown, pink (top $100.00)	175.00–200.00
	#3	Unknown, crystal (top $10.00)	15.00– 20.00
	#4	Unknown, frosted crystal "Baby's Orange"	50.00– 65.00
	#5	Unknown, crystal	25.00– 35.00
	#6	Unknown, frosted crystal decorated "Baby"	85.00– 95.00
Row 6:	#1	Unknown, crystal	35.00– 40.00
	#2	Unknown, crystal, called "Button & Bows"	45.00– 60.00
	#3	Unknown, crystal probably foreign (emb. sword & hammer)	30.00– 35.00
	#4	Unknown, crystal, "thumbprint" design	45.00– 50.00
	#5	Unknown, crystal, notched top	45.00– 50.00
	#6	Unknown, crystal	30.00– 40.00
Row 7:	#1	Unknown, decorated crystal, "Orange Juice"	55.00– 60.00
	#2	Unknown, frosted decorated crystal	85.00–100.00
	#3	Unknown, pink (possibly foreign)	125.00–150.00
	#4	Fenton, SCA (sun-colored-amethyst) (bottom $55.00)	70.00– 80.00
	#5	Fenton, elephant decorated base	65.00– 75.00

REAMERS, Fenton, Fry, Foreign, Federal and Indiana

The following three pages show the vast price ranges reamer collectors face. Reamers come in all shapes, sizes, and colors. The names in quotes with the Fry reamers are the company names for each color.

The foreign reamers on page 150 represent a separate collecting field in themselves. Not enough information is known about this vast field of reamers. There are many unique shapes and colors to attract a collector to these reamers made outside the United States.

Page 149

Row 1:	#1	Fenton pitcher & reamer set, red	1,000.00–1,200.00
		(top is ⅓ price; bottom is ⅔ on these)	
	#2	Same, black	1,200.00–1,400.00
	#3	Same, blue	1,750.00–2,000.00
	#4	Same, jade	750.00– 850.00
Row 2:	#1	Same, transparent green, top only	200.00– 225.00
	#2	Fry, straight side, "Azure" blue	1,500.00–1,600.00
	#3	Same, light green	20.00– 22.50
	#4	Same, "Emerald" green	25.00– 30.00
Row 3:	#1	Same, "Pearl" opalescent white	22.00– 25.00

Row 3:		(Continued)	
		Same, embossed "Blue Goose"	175.00–200.00
	#2	Same, "Canary" vaseline	40.00– 45.00
	#3	Same, "Rose" pink	45.00– 55.00
Row 4:	#1	Same, crystal	10.00– 12.50
	#2	Same, "Amber"	300.00–325.00
	#3	Same, "China" white	600.00–800.00
Row 5:	#1	Fry, fluted reamer (jello mold) "Canary"	250.00–275.00
	#2	Same, "Emerald" green	450.00–500.00
	#3	Same, "Rose"	150.00–175.00
Row 6:	#1	Same, "Pearl"	30.00– 35.00
	#2, 3	Tufglas, light or dark	75.00– 85.00

Foreign Reamers
Page 150

Row 1:	#1	Pinkish amber	40.00– 45.00
	#2, 5	Cobalt blue or amber	100.00–110.00
	#3	Smoke	75.00– 85.00
	#4	Yellowish custard	90.00–100.00
Row 2:	#1, 5	Pink or light pinkish amber	40.00– 50.00
	#2, 3	Embossed "Foreign," 2 piece, green or pink	40.00– 50.00
	#4	Yellow	125.00–140.00
Row 3:	#1, 3, 5	Root Beer, blue & light yellow, ea.	100.00–110.00
	#2	Embossed "Tcheco-Scovaquie" on handle, crystal	40.00– 50.00
	#4	Embossed sword & hammer on handle	15.00– 20.00
Row 4:	#1, 5	Crystal, last has "K" inside shield mark, ea.	15.00– 20.00
	#2	Light yellow top only	65.00– 75.00
	#3, 4	Pink or "Coke" bottle green	45.00– 55.00

Row 5:	#1, 2, 4 & 5	Light green, amber, amethyst or pinkish amber, ea.	60.00– 70.00
	#3	Crystal	25.00– 30.00
Row 6:	#1	Light turquoise	50.00– 55.00
	#2	Green, marked "Argentina"	125.00–150.00
	#3, 5	Cornflower blue or light green	100.00–125.00
	#4	Crystal, embossed fruit	50.00– 60.00
Row 7:	#1, 2	Crystal Czechoslovakia or pink	40.00– 50.00
	#3, 4	Light turquoise or diamond shaped crystal (Rb No 517385)	35.00– 40.00
	#5	Pink	90.00–110.00
	#6	Amber	100.00–110.00

Page 151
Rows 1-3 Federal Glass Company

Row 1:	#1	Ribbed, loop handle, pink	25.00– 30.00
	#2	Same, amber	17.50– 20.00
	#3	Panelled, loop handle, green	22.50– 25.00
Row 2:	#1	Same, amber	17.50– 20.00
	#2	Tab handle, yellowish/-amber	275.00–300.00
	#3	Same, green	12.00– 15.00
	#4	Tab handled, ribbed, seed dam, green	12.50– 15.00
Row 3:	#1	Same, pink	90.00–100.00
	#2, 3	Tab handled amber, ea.	12.50– 15.00
	#4	Green, pointed cone	12.50– 15.00

Rows 4-6 Indiana Glass Company

Row 4:	#1	Amber, handled, spout opposite	250.00–300.00
	#2	Same, crystal	10.00– 12.00
	#3	Same, pink	60.00– 70.00
Row 5:	#1	Same, green	32.00– 35.00
	#2	Crystal, horizontal handle	10.00– 12.50
	#3	Same, green	18.00– 20.00
Row 6:	#1	Crystal, emb. ASCO, "Good Morning, Orange Juice"	18.00– 20.00
	#2	Amber, six sided cone, vertical handle	250.00–300.00
	#3	Same, green	35.00– 40.00
	#4	Same, pink	125.00–150.00

REAMERS, Hazel Atlas and Hocking Glass Companies

The Hazel Atlas 2-cup reamer pitcher has been the plague of novice collectors and dealers for several years. This has been newly made in cobalt blue, pink, and an odd green color. **See Reproduction Section on pages 236 – 237 for items with asterisk.**

Page 153 All Hazel Atlas Glass Company

Row 1:	#1	Yellow 2 cup pitcher and reamer set	275.00–300.00
	#2	Same, cobalt blue	*250.00–275.00
	#3	Same, pink	*110.00–125.00
	#4	Same, green	*25.00– 30.00
Row 2:	#1	Crisscross, cobalt blue	250.00–275.00
	#2	Same, pink	225.00–250.00
	#3	Same, crystal	10.00– 12.00
	#4	Same, green	18.00– 20.00
Row 3:	#1	Green, tab handled	10.00– 12.00
	#2, 3	Decorated 2 cup sets, ea.	35.00– 38.00
	#4	Fired-on red set	40.00– 45.00
Row 4:	#1, 3-5	Decorated sets, ea.	35.00– 38.00
	#2	Tumbler to match #1	8.00– 10.00
Row 5:	#1	Crisscross, tab handled, pink	275.00–300.00
	#2	Same, green	18.00– 20.00
	#3	Same, crystal	10.00– 12.00
	#4	Green, tab handled	8.00– 10.00

Page 154 All Hazel Atlas Glass Company

Row 1:	#1	Reamer pit., 4 cup marked A&J, green	30.00– 35.00
	#2	Same, A & J, Pat Applied For, crystal	18.00– 20.00
	#3	Green, 4 cup, ftd.	30.00– 35.00
	#4	Green, stippled pitcher	30.00– 35.00
Row 2:	#1, 2	Tab handle, lemon, pink, light or dark	35.00– 40.00
	#3	Same, green	12.00– 15.00
	#4	Same, white w/red trim	22.50– 25.00
Row 3:	#1-3	White, w/decorated trim, 4 cup	30.00– 35.00
	#4	White, 4 cup, stippled pitcher	27.50– 32.50
Row 4:	#1	Small tab handled reamer, pink	35.00– 40.00
	#2	Same, green	12.00– 15.00
	#3	Same, cobalt blue	250.00–300.00
	#4	Large tab handled reamer, pink	30.00– 35.00
Row 5:	#1	Same, white	35.00– 40.00
	#2	Same, cobalt blue	250.00–275.00
	#3	Same, crystal	4.50– 5.00
	#4	Same, green	12.00– 15.00

Page 155 All Hocking or Anchor Hocking Glass Company

Row 1:	#1	"Circle" pitcher w/reamer top	65.00– 70.00
	#2	Pitcher reamer, 4 cup, ftd., green	30.00– 35.00
	#3	Pitcher reamer, 4 cup, flat, green	25.00– 30.00
Row 2:	#1	Pitcher reamer, 2 cup, green	25.00– 27.50
	#2	Same, Vitrock	25.00– 30.00
	#3	Pitcher reamer, ribbed, 2 cup	55.00– 60.00
	#4	Same, crystal	22.50– 25.00
Row 3:	#1	Pitcher reamer, 4 cup, crystal	25.00– 27.50
	#2	Vitrock, tab	85.00–100.00
	#3	Green "Clambroth," tab	115.00–125.00
	#4	Pitcher top, "Mayfair blue"	250.00–300.00
Row 4:	#1-3	Orange reamer, loop handle, green, ea.	15.00– 20.00
Row 5:	#1	Same, Vitrock	18.00– 20.00
	#2	Fired-on black tab	12.50– 15.00
	#3	Green tab	12.00– 15.00

REAMERS, Fleur-de-Lis, Jeannette, and Miscellaneous

The reamers shown on Page 157 are found mainly on the West coast. I am astonished at the diversity of tints of opaque red found on Fleur-de-Lis reamers. A fleur-de-lis emblem is embossed on the side of most of these. (If not, it is listed as unembossed.) The opalescent red shades are quite stunning particularly when they are exhibited in an illuminated cabinet.

Price differences are controlled by color variations, whether there are emblems or not or whether the reamers possess rims or not.

Note the large Delphite reamer Row 3, #4 on Page 159. There have been few of these found!

Page 157

Row	#	Description	Price
Row 1:	#1	"VALENCIA," white (embossed word)	90.00–100.00
	#2	Same, crystal	150.00–200.00
	#3	Same, green	175.00–200.00
Row 2:	#1	Plain, no embossing, "VALENCIA"	75.00– 85.00
	#2	Same, opalescent white	50.00– 60.00
	#3	Same, pink	150.00–200.00
	#4	Same, pinkish amber	250.00–300.00
Row 3:	#1, 4	"Fleur-de-Lis," red/orange slag	350.00–425.00
	#2	Same, amberina/opalescent	550.00–650.00
	#3	Same, mustard/slag	375.00–450.00
Row 4:	#1	Embossed white "Fleur-de-Lis"	75.00– 85.00
	#2	Same, red/orange slag	350.00–425.00
	#3	Same, red	425.00–500.00
	#4	Same, root beer	550.00–600.00
Row 5:	#1	Same, crystal	175.00–200.00
	#2	Unembossed, grayish custard	125.00–150.00
	#3	Same, custard w/"rim edge"	135.00–150.00
	#4	Same, white w/"rim edge"	40.00– 60.00
Row 6:	#1	"LINDSAY," pink	375.00–425.00
	#2	"LINDSEY," pink	375.00–425.00
	#3	"LINDSAY," green	400.00–450.00

Page 158

Row	#	Description	Price
Row 1:	#1	Large crystal (called "monster")	35.00– 40.00
	#2	Light turquoise, O J extractor	100.00–125.00
	#3	Foreign, pink	65.00– 75.00
	#4	Crystal, Glasbake, McKee on handle	50.00– 75.00
Row 2:	#1	Hazel Atlas old reamer (recently iridized)	60.00– 75.00
	#2	Green "log" handle	100.00–125.00
	#3	Crystal	10.00– 12.50
	#4	"Colony" like, twin spout	*15.00– 20.00
		Same, white	150.00–200.00
	#5	Foreign, amber	60.00– 70.00
Row 3:	#1	"Clambroth," "British make," embossed	175.00–200.00
	#2	"MacBeth-Evans Glass Co., Charleroi, Pa."	350.00–400.00
	#3	"Clambroth," boat shaped	150.00–200.00
Row 4:	#1	Black, "Orange Juice Extractor"	350.00–400.00
	#2	Same, green	45.00– 50.00
	#3	Same, pink	100.00–125.00
	#4	Same, "Clambroth"	75.00– 8500
Row 5:	#1	Green, like #2, but unembossed	150.00–200.00
	#2	Crystal, embossed "Sunkist Oranges & Lemons" or "Los Angeles Fruit Growers Exchange," ea.	25.00– 35.00
	#3	Pink, unembossed	185.00–200.00
Row 6:	#1	Crystal, square, marked Italy	12.50– 15.00
	#2	"Easley's," (called "chisel cone")	65.00– 75.00
	#3	"Easley's," square opalescent white	150.00–200.00
	#4	"Read," some embossed, some not	100.00–125.00
	#5	Unusual six sided top	45.00– 50.00

Page 159 All Jeannette Glass Company

Row	#	Description	Price
Row 1:	#1	"Hex Optic" bucket reamer, pink	40.00– 45.00
	#2	Same, green	40.00– 45.00
	#3	2 cup reamer pitcher	100.00– 110.00
	#4	Delphite, w/top (see page 24)	1,250.00–1,500.00
Row 2:	#1	Crystal, large, loop handle	8.00– 10.00
	#2	Same, green	20.00– 22.00
	#3	2 cup reamer pitcher, light Jadite	20.00– 22.50
	#4	Same, dark Jadite matching top/bottom	60.00– 75.00
Row 3:	#1	Small, Delphite	65.00– 75.00
	#2	Large, dark Jadite	20.00– 25.00
	#3	Same, light Jadite	18.00– 20.00
	#4	Same, Delphite	1,000.00–1,250.00
Row 4:	#1	Small, dark Jadite	22.00– 25.00
	#2	Same, light Jadite	20.00– 22.00
	#3	"Jennyware," crystal	75.00– 85.00
	#4	Same, pink	90.00– 100.00
	#5	Same, ultra-marine	100.00– 110.00
Row 5:	#1	Green, 5" tab reamer	12.00– 15.00
	#2	Green, 5⅞" tab reamer	12.50– 15.00
	#3	Same as #1, crystal	8.00– 10.00
	#4	Same as #2, pink	35.00– 40.00
	#5	Same as #1, pink	35.00– 40.00

REAMERS, Cambridge and McKee

McKee Glass Company made most of the Sunkist reamers, though not all. **According to records just uncovered at the Fenton factory, the very first Sunkist reamers were made by Indiana Glass Company.**

The McKee symbol is an "McK" with a circle around it and said insignia adds interest to a reamer. Collectors of reamers concern themselves with color, type (lemon, orange, grapefruit), handles, spouts, seed dams or not, footed or flat bottomed, embossing, size and shape of the reaming section, etc. As usual, scarcity and demand determine price for reamers, many of which are not cheap!

Page 161

Row 1:	#1	Cambridge green	175.00– 200.00
	#2, 3	Same, light pink	175.00– 200.00
Row 2:	#1	Same, amber	600.00– 700.00
	#2	Same, green w/silver Rockwell decoration	250.00– 300.00
	#3	Cambridge, crystal	20.00– 25.00
		Same, Cobalt blue (shown page 21)	2,000.00–2,500.00
Row 3:	#1	Cambridge, small tab, crystal	12.50– 15.00
	#2	Same, cobalt blue	250.00– 300.00
	#3	Cambridge, small, ftd., green	400.00– 450.00
		Same, crystal, (not shown)	15.00– 18.00

Row 3:		(Continued)	
		Same, pink, (not shown)	350.00–400.00
		Same, cobalt blue, (not shown)	750.00– 850.00
	#4	Grapefruit, ultra-marine	550.00– 600.00
Row 4:	#1	Same, Seville yellow	210.00– 225.00
	#2	Same, flat yellow	225.00– 250.00
	#3	Same, custard	600.00– 650.00
Row 5:	#1	Same, "Caramel"	750.00– 850.00
	#2	Same, black	900.00–1,100.00
	#3	Same, white	250.00– 350.00
Row 6:	#1	Same, Jadite	135.00– 150.00
	#2	Same, Chalaine blue	700.00– 800.00
	#3	Same, pink	600.00– 650.00

Page 162 All embossed "SUNKIST" unless noted.

Row 1:	#1	Green opalescent "fry"	175.00–195.00
	#2	Opalescent "fry"	85.00– 95.00
	#3	Transparent ultra-marine	650.00–700.00
	#4	Butterscotch "fry"	650.00–700.00
Row 2:	#1	Lilac pinkish white	75.00– 85.00
	#2	Pink	50.00– 60.00
	#3	Light pink	50.00– 60.00
	#4	Pinkish amber	175.00–185.00
Row 3:	#1	"Blocked" letters in "SUNKIST," swirl	300.00–350.00
	#2	Black	600.00–700.00
	#3	Chalaine blue	175.00–195.00
	#4	Chocolate	500.00–600.00
Row 4:	#1	Turquoise blue milk glass	250.00–350.00

Row 4:		(Continued)	
	#2	Jadite	20.00– 22.00
	#3	Dark Jadite, slightly opalescent	150.00–165.00
	#4	Olive green milk glass	600.00–650.00
Row 5:	#1	Transparent green	45.00– 50.00
	#2	Unembossed green	200.00–250.00
	#3	Forest Green	450.00–500.00
	#4	Vaseline green	40.00– 50.00
Row 6:	#1	Seville yellow	40.00– 55.00
	#2	Yellowish custard	30.00– 35.00
	#3	Custard	25.00– 30.00
	#4	Greenish custard	75.00– 85.00

Page 163 "SUNKIST" Rows 1-3

Row 1:	#1	Ivory	125.00–150.00
	#2	Gray	135.00–150.00
	#3	Opal white (value determined by opalescence)	35.00–100.00
	#4	White	7.00– 10.00
Row 2:	#1	"Blocked" letters in "SUNKIST," white	75.00 90.00
	#2	Opal Crown Tuscan	250.00–300.00
	#3	Crown Tuscan milk glass	250.00–300.00
	#4	Caramel variation	250.00–300.00
Row 3:	#1	Caramel, light	250.00–300.00
	#2	Caramel, medium	300.00–350.00
	#3	Caramel, butterscotch	300.00–350.00
	#4	Mustard	300.00–350.00
Row 4:	#1	Skokie Green, pointed cone, 5¼"	50.00– 55.00

Row 4:		(Continued)	
	#2	Same, Custard	45.00– 50.00
	#3	Jadite, unembossed, smaller foot than embossed below in Row 6	22.50– 25.00
Row 5:	#1	White, "McK" embossed	18.00– 20.00
	#2	Same, Custard	18.00– 20.00
	#3	Same, Jadite	20.00– 22.50
	#4	Same, Delphite	225.00–275.00
Row 6:	#1	White, 6", "McK" embossed	30.00– 35.00
	#2	Same, Custard w/red trim	20.00– 25.00
	#3	Same, Jadite	25.00– 28.00
	#4	Same, Delphite	450.00–500.00

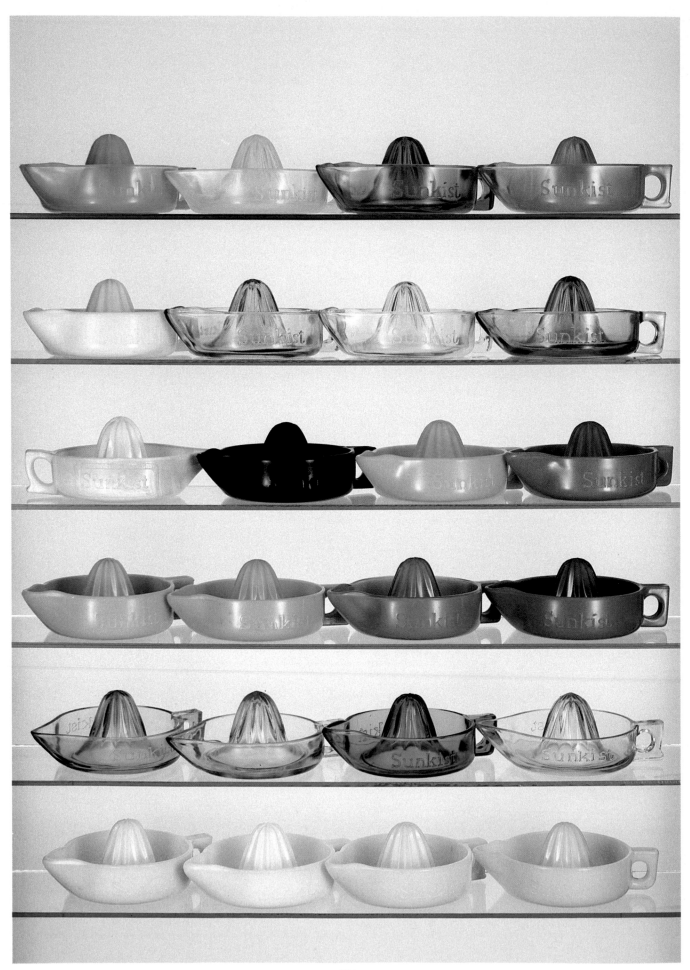

REAMERS, Paden City, Westmoreland, and U.S. Glass Companies

You can find numerous cocktail shaker bottoms missing their metal reamer tops. That metal top is a hard to find item, so don't buy too many topless cocktail shakers expecting to find a top. To my knowledge, there are no replacements for these available. See **Reproduction Section pages 236 – 237** for items with asterisks.

There are *several different* inserts for the U.S. Glass reamers. The pitcher in Row 1, #1 and the tubs in Row 2 on Page 166 each have a 4½" diameter reamer top. A 4⅛" top fits the other pitchers on Page 166 *and* the slick handled, horizontal ribbed two cup pitchers on that page. That 4⅛" top fits all the loop handled two cup pitchers on Page 167, but the insert for the four cup pitchers is 5⅛" in diameter.

Page 165

Row 1:	#1	Pink cocktail shaker/ reamer, "Party Line"	60.00– 65.00
	#2	Same, amber	100.00–110.00
	#3	Green, cocktail shaker/ reamer, "Speakeasy"	40.00– 45.00
	#4	Pink pitcher & reamer top	200.00–250.00
		Same, crystal pitcher w/black handle & top (shown page 171)	300.00–350.00
	#5	Green, 4 cup pitcher & top, "Party Line"	80.00– 95.00
Row 2:	#1	Same, pink	110.00–125.00
	#2	Same, crystal complete	60.00– 65.00
		Same, turquoise blue complete	350.00–400.00
		Same, black (shown page 171)	500.00–550.00

Row 2:	(Continued)		
	#3	Westmoreland, green, 2 piece, embossed orange/lemon	*150.00–175.00
	#4	Same, pink	*150.00–175.00
Row 3:	#1	Same, crystal	*175.00–195.00
	#2, 3	Westmoreland, crystal decorated oranges or lemons, flattened loop handle, ea	*55.00– 65.00
Row 4:	#1	Same, dark green	*90.00–110.00
	#2	Same, light green	*90.00–110.00
	#3	Same, bluish green	*125.00–140.00
Row 5:	#1	Same, white	*200.00–250.00
	#2	Same, pink	*75.00– 85.00
	#3	Same, amber	*200.00–250.00

Page 166 All U.S. Glass Company

Row 1:	#1, 4	Reamer pitcher set, 3 piece, pink, ea.	250.00–275.00
	#2	Reamer pitcher set, green	250.00–275.00
		Same, yellow, shown on page 87	650.00–750.00
	#3	Tumbler for set	10.00– 12.50
Row 2:	#1	Tub, w/reamer top, pink	150.00–200.00
	#2	Same, green	150.00–200.00
	#3	"Vidrio Products No. J-50"	150.00–165.00
	#4	Slick handle, 2 piece, horizontal ribs, (each rib is ½ cup) amber	200.00–300.00
Row 3:	#1	Slick handle, green, insert near top of cup (graduated measurements on side)	30.00– 35.00

Row 3:	(Continued)		
	#2	Same, pink	30.00– 35.00
	#3	Same as Row 2, #4, pink	32.00– 35.00
	#4	Same, frosted pink	20.00– 25.00
Row 4:	#1	Same, green	30.00– 35.00
	#2	Same, turquoise blue	85.00–100.00
	#3	Same, crystal	20.00– 22.50
	#4	Same, frosted green	25.00– 28.00
Row 5:	#1	Slick handle, barred or vertical ribs	40.00– 50.00
	#2	"Handy Andy," green (note reamer cone differs)	40.00– 50.00
	#3	Crystal, same as #1	15.00– 18.00

Page 167 All U.S. Glass Company

Row 1:	#1	4 cup pitcher set, amber	500.00–550.00
	#2	Same, green	110.00–120.00
	#3	Same, pink	250.00–275.00
Row 2:	#1	2 cup, pitcher set, light pink	40.00– 45.00
	#2	Same, dark pink	40.00– 45.00
	#3	Same, white	125.00–150.00
	#4	Same, amber	250.00–300.00
Row 3:	#1	Same, yellow (light honey amber)	250.00–300.00
	#2	Same, blue complete	600.00–750.00
		Same, crystal, complete	15.00– 17.50
	#3, 5	Same, crystal, decorated, ea.	20.00– 25.00

Row 3:	(Continued)		
	#4	Tumbler, matching reamer	5.00– 7.50
Row 4:	#1	Same, frosted green	22.00– 25.00
	#2	Same, bluish green (turquoise)	100.00–115.00
	#3	Same, dark green	40.00– 45.00
	#4	Same, light green	35.00– 40.00
Row 5:	#1	Slick handle, light pink	100.00–110.00
	#2	Same, dark pink	90.00–110.00
	#3	Same, amber	300.00–325.00
Row 6:	#1	Same, white	60.00– 65.00
	#2	Same, green	75.00– 85.00
	#3	Slick handle, grapefruit	400.00–450.00

REAMERS, Miscellaneous, Mechanical and Unusual

This remains the "catch-all" section on reamers. Reamers not fitting previous categories go here. Many of the glass reamer manufactures are unknown, although I am sure that McKee made the Saunders and most likely the Radnt. However, to my knowledge, no valid catalogue information has ever surfaced to prove that.

I shall repeat the RE-GO reamer story as shown in Rows 3 and 5 on page 169. I find it unbelievable that these ever survived being used. It is a mechanical, glass, two part reamer. The only thing separating the glass from crunching together is a small wooden peg that allows the insert to be turned by hand to extract the juice.

The name RE-GO comes from a reamer that originally said "puRE-GOld." (The small letters in pure gold were placed there for emphasis by me.) The PURE-GOLD reamer itself may never have been marketed; the first name was altered by removing the letters "p, u, l, d" to leave the name RE-GO. The old letters can still be seen on these reamers, albeit slightly.

The green insert shown in Row 3 #1 is called "EASY SQUEEZE" and is used on a similar base as that of the RE-GO.

The crystal pitcher on Page 171 in Row 2, #3 has to have a **black handle** and **black top** for price listed.

Page 169

Row 1:	#1	Jadite, embossed SAUNDERS	1,000.00–1,250.00
	#2	"Sanitary Bess Mixer," (embossed **"4"** inside a large **"1"**)	175.00– 200.00
	#3	"Ideal" Pat'd Jan 31, 1888	125.00– 175.00
	#4	Black, same as #1	1,000.00–1,250.00
Row 2:	#1	"Tricia," black	1,200.00–1,400.00
	#2	Same, pink complete	700.00– 800.00
		Same, crystal complete	350.00– 400.00
	#3	Same, green	600.00– 700.00
Row 3:	#1	"EASY SQUEEZE," green top only	200.00– 250.00
		Same, complete (not shown)	500.00– 550.00
	#2	Green RE-GO	400.00– 500.00
	#3	RE-GO crystal top only	125.00– 150.00
		Same, complete (not shown)	300.00– 400.00
Row 4:	#1	"RADNT," crystal	95.00– 115.00
	#2	Same, green	350.00– 450.00
	#3	Same, pink	350.00– 450.00
Row 5:	#1	RE-GO, opalescent white	550.00– 650.00
	#2	Same, blue	1000.00–1,250.00
	#3	Same, black (top shown)	1000.00–1,250.00

Page 170

Row 1:	#1	Metal insert	75.00– 85.00
	#2	Glass insert, probably Hocking	225.00–250.00
	#3	Mount Joy	150.00–175.00
Row 2:	#1	"Mayfair" blue glass insert, probably Hocking	400.00–450.00
	#2	"SUNKIST JUNIOR" mechanical reamer, "clambroth"	100.00–125.00

Page 171

Row 1:	#1	Hocking "Mayfair" blue 2 cup reamer pitcher	1,400.00–1,500.00
Row 2:	#1	Paden City "Party Line", black	500.00– 550.00
	#2	Morgantown, green	200.00– 250.00
	#3	Morgantown, crystal pitcher, black handle & top	300.00– 350.00

171

ROLLING PINS

Rolling pin reproductions have caused my mail box to fill up for about two years. A word of warning to those of you who may have found a colored rolling pin with a screw-on metal lid. No "old" rolling pins with screw-on metal lids have ever been found in any transparent color other than crystal. If you have pink, cobalt blue, red, or an odd shade of green, then you have a "recent vintage" rolling pin!

The abundance of crystal rolling pins has not noticeably diminished. These sell in the $10.00–12.00 range. Dealers who sell primitives or crafts are filling these with marbles, beans, and other colorful things to sell them. I saw one around Easter with jelly beans priced at $25.00!

Shown below are some new additions to the listing: black and "Robin Egg" blue. Both of these are the blown type shown on page 175.

Page 172

Row 1: #1 Black   400.00–450.00
       #2 "Robin Egg" blue   400.00–450.00

Page 173 McKee Glass Company except for last row

Row 1: Note circular band opposite shaker top end.
     #1 Jadite   350.00–400.00
     #2 Custard   275.00–325.00

Row 2 & 3: Note smooth end opposite shaker top end on these rows.

#1 Seville yellow   275.00– 325.00
#2 Delphite blue   1,500.00–1,800.00
Row 3: #1 Chalaine blue   1,500.00–1,800.00
     #2 Jadite   350.00– 400.00
Row 4: #1 Crystal w/screw-on cobalt handles   225.00– 250.00

Wooden Handles
Page 174

Row 1:   Peacock blue (handles attached to metal rod inside pin)   250.00–275.00
Row 2: #1 Green transparent (handles attached to wood dowel pin)   400.00–450.00
     #2 Pink (screw-on wooden handles)   400.00–450.00
Row 3: #1 White (comes w/wood or metal screw-on handles), ea. marked "Imperial Mfg. Co., Cambridge, Ohio"   45.00– 50.00
        Same, Custard color (not shown)   140.00–165.00
     #2 Cobalt blue (handles attached to metal rod inside pin)   400.00–450.00
Row 4:   Clambroth white (screw-on wood handles)   100.00–125.00

Blown Rolling Pins
Page 175

Row 1: #1 Amethyst   120.00–135.00
     #2 Cobalt blue   150.00–200.00
Row 2: #1 Amber, light   100.00–120.00
     #2 Forest green   125.00–150.00

Row 3: #1 Peacock blue, dark   175.00–200.00
     #2 Crystal, "Kardov Flour, Famous Self Rising"   50.00– 60.00
Row 4: #1 Chalaine blue   400.00–450.00
     #2 Blue, light   175.00–225.00

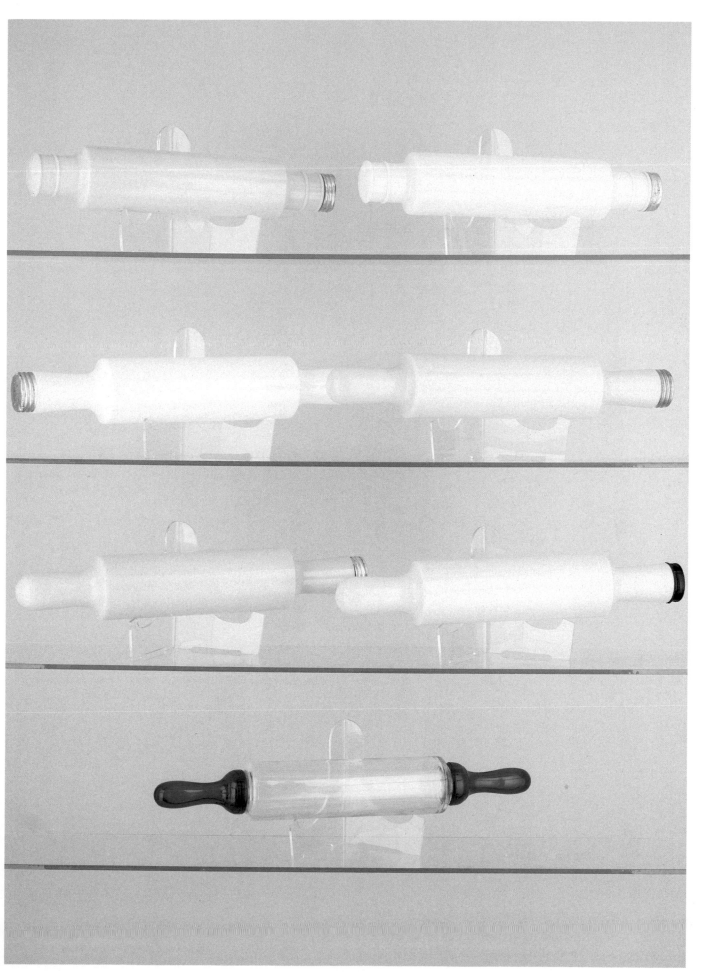

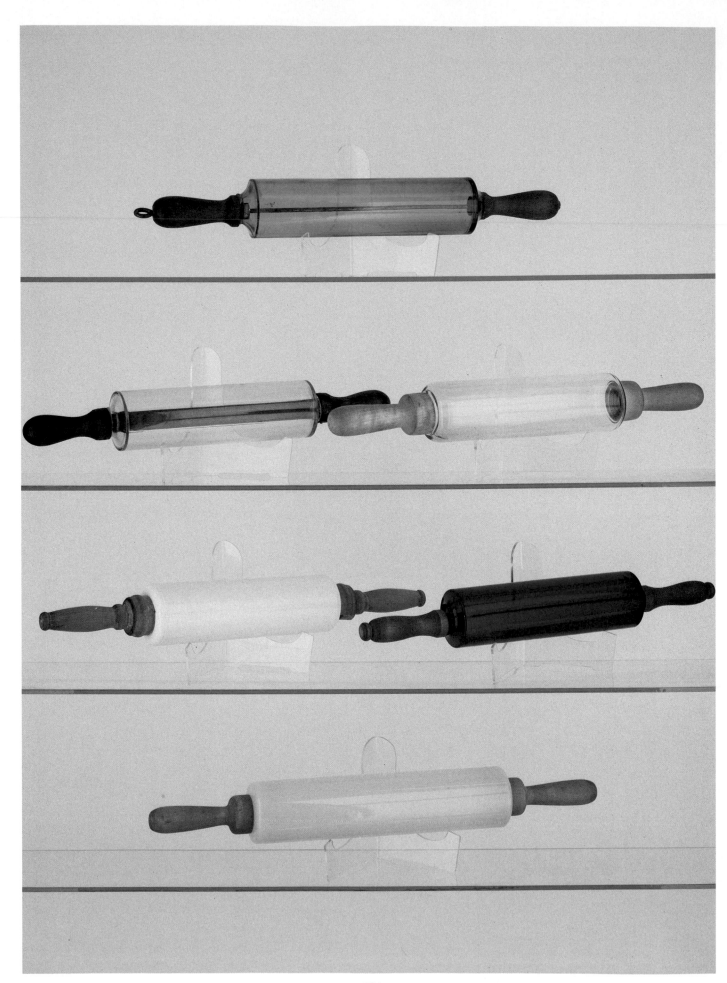

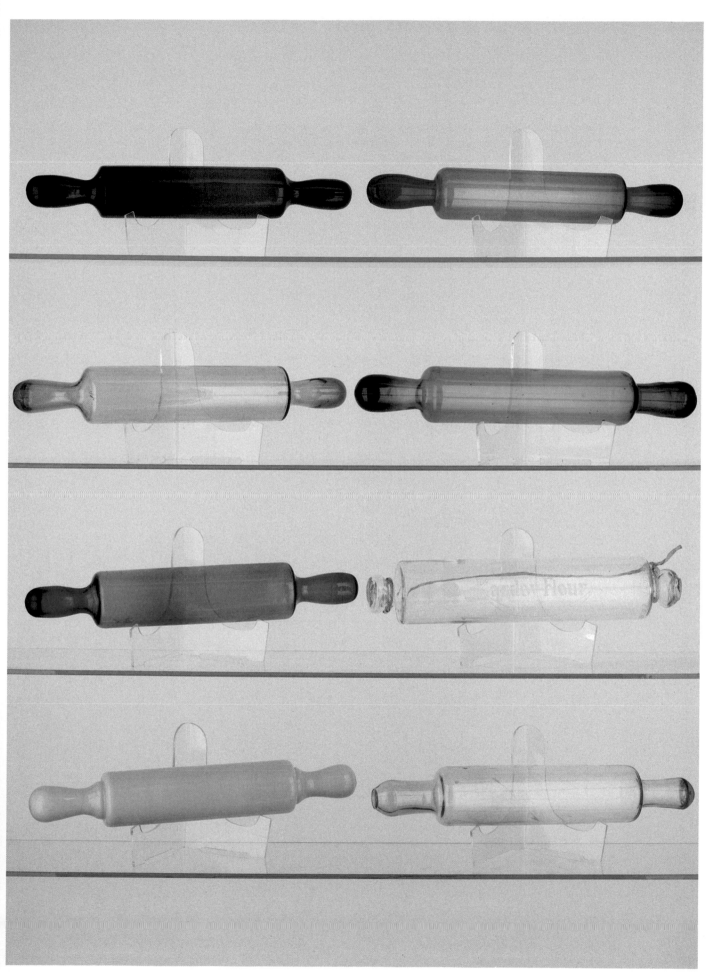

SALAD SETS and ADDITIONAL LADLES

Prices of the colored sets have soared, especially those from the Cambridge, Imperial, or Heisey companies. Items made by major glass companies of that time are always more collectable than unidentified glassware.

The inclusion of salad sets in the Kitchen book opened a new collecting field for some buyers who were not aware of the variety available before then. Many of these sets were of foreign manufacture — mainly Czechoslovakia.

Forks and spoons sell for around the same price, but there seems to be a small premium ($1.00–5.00) for a set. A few remaining ladles that would not fit in that section are included on page 179.

Prices below are for sets unless otherwise noted. (Take half of the lowest price listed for one piece only.)

Page 177

Row 1:	#1	Blue, large pointed handle set	50.00–60.00
	#2	Amber set	30.00–40.00
	#3	Yellow, small pointed handle set	30.00–40.00
		Same, pink (not shown) marked "TCHECOBLOV"	40.00–50.00
	#4, 5	Green set	40.00–50.00
	#6-9	Same, peacock or cobalt blue set	55.00–70.00
	#10	Same, red set	75.00–85.00
	#11, 12	Boxed forks, green or pink, ea	25.00–30.00
Row 2:	#1, 2	Long crystal handled amber set	30.00–35.00
	#3, 4	Red teardrop handle set	50.00–60.00
		Same, cobalt blue (not shown)	45.00–55.00
		Same, amethyst (not shown)	40.00–50.00
	#5	Green top and bottom set	40.00–50.00
	#6	Blue spoon	27.50–35.00
	#7, 8	Green set	50.00–60.00
	#9	Amber flattened stripped handle set	30.00–40.00
Row 3:	#1, 2	Forest green set	40.00–45.00
	#3, 4	Black handled set	55.00–65.00
	#5, 6	All amber set, found with Czechoslovakia labels	40.00–50.00
	#7	White set, serrated and waffle back	40.00–50.00
	#8	Canary yellow or vaseline, set	70.00–80.00

Page 178

Row 1:	#1, 2	Cobalt blue, rounded, ribbed handle set	50.00–55.00
	#3, 4	Same, green	40.00–45.00
	#5, 6	Same, light blue	50.00–55.00
	#7, 8	Same, amber	25.00–35.00
	#9	Same, crystal	20.00–22.50
		Same, pink (not shown)	40.00–45.00
Row 2:	#1	Blue w/crystal top, set	45.00–50.00
	#2, 3	Forest green flattened handle set	45.00–55.00
	#4, 5	Pink set, edge down sides	45.00–50.00
	#6, 7	Same, cobalt blue	50.00–55.00
	#8, 9	Same, amber	30.00–35.00
Row 3:	#1	Blue pointed fork, set	45.00–55.00
	#2, 3	Amber flattened handle set	30.00–35.00
	#4	Same, pink	45.00–50.00
	#5, 6	Same, green	45.00–50.00
	#7, 8	Amber set	35.00–40.00
	#9-11	Amber 3 piece set	65.00–75.00
		Same, cake server only	35.00–40.00

Page 179

Row 1:	**All Cambridge Glass Company**		
	#1, 2	Crystal set w/label	40.00– 45.00
	#3-6	Black or light blue	125.00–150.00
	#7, 8	Amber	65.00– 75.00
	#9	Green set	100.00–110.00
	#10	Red set	175.00–200.00
		Same, cobalt blue (not shown)	200.00–250.00
Row 2:	#1, 2	Light blue set, **Imperial** (box shown $5.00)	75.00– 85.00
	#3, 4	Same, amber	55.00– 65.00
	#5, 6	Same, green	75.00– 85.00
	#7, 8	Pink set, possibly Imperial	75.00– 85.00
	#9, 10	Same, blue	100.00–110.00
Row 3:	**Ladles**		
	#1	Green	35.00– 45.00
	#2	Same, crystal	30.00– 35.00
	#3	White, black handle/measure on side of ladle	45.00– 50.00
	#4	Crystal, large	12.00– 15.00

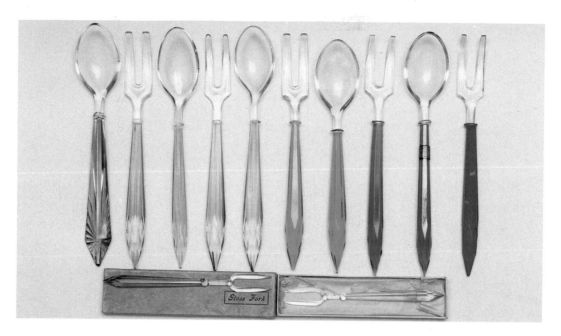

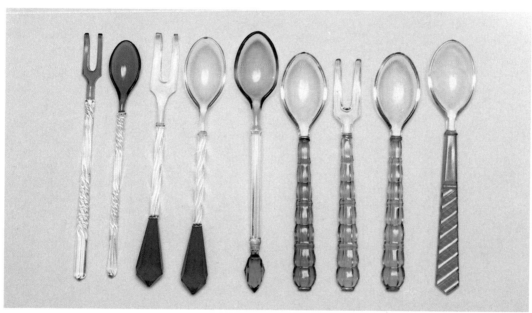

177

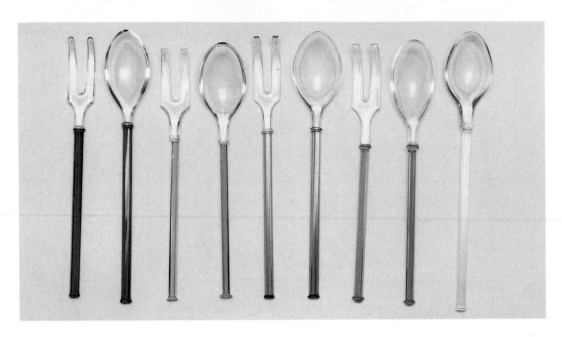

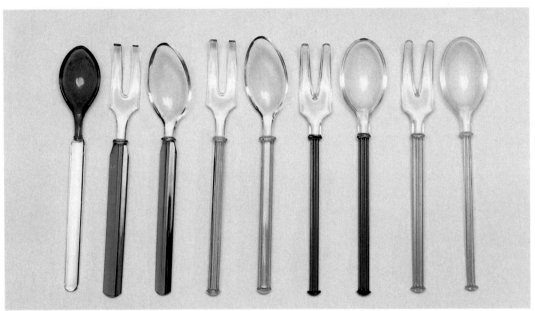

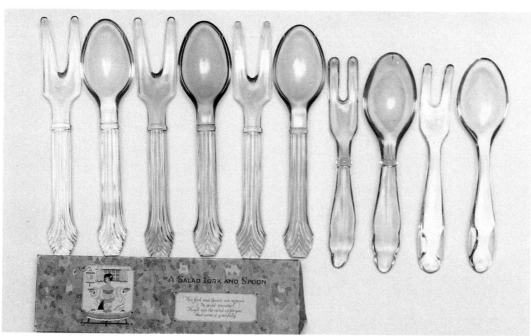

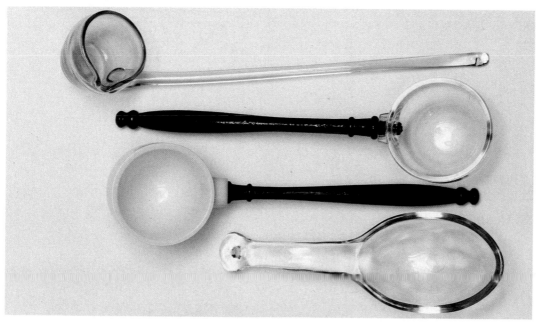

179

SALT BOXES

Salt boxes are another of the items that few collectors buy per se, but many are bought by collectors of color or by collectors buying sets. The "Zipper" or the "Sneath" canister sets are not complete without the salts shown here. There is considerable demand for these latter types and they sell very quickly on the market.

Crystal salt boxes are gathered by collectors looking to complete "Hoosier" or comparable kitchen cabinet spice and canister sets. I have seen some very high prices on these in shops that sell "primitive" antiques. What I wonder is, "Do they actually sell for those prices?"

Row 1:	#1	Crystal w/glass lid, embossed SALT, Flintext	80.00– 90.00
	#2	Jadite, Mckee	75.00– 85.00
	#3	Same, Chalaine blue	175.00–200.00
Row 2:	#1	Green "Zipper" w/lid	125.00–150.00
		Same, wo/lid	100.00–125.00
	#2	Peacock blue	125.00–150.00
	#3	Green "Sneath"	225.00–250.00
Row 3:	#1	Jadite w/lid, Jeannette	195.00–225.00
	#2	White, embossed SALT box	100.00–125.00
	#3	White, round embossed SALT box	75.00– 85.00
Row 4:	#1	Crystal, "Sneath"	15.00– 20.00
	#2	Amber "Sneath"	125.00–150.00
	#3	Crystal, embossed SALT	12.00– 15.00
	#4	Crystal, "Zipper"	10.00– 12.00
Row 5:	#1	Green Jeannette round embossed SALT on lid	165.00–175.00
	#2	Crystal salt w/lid	15.00– 17.50
	#3	Crystal, ribbed, embossed SALT	10.00– 12.50
	#4	Crystal, ribbed	8.00– 12.00

SHAKERS, Hocking, Hazel Atlas, Owens Illinois, Tipp City

Please note that the previously listed "kitchen cabinet shakers" shown on page 185 Row 4, #5, 6 were strictly vacuum cleaner attachments used for blowing moth crystals into your closet. Two readers have definitely confirmed this with vacuum advertising! Live and learn!

See Reproduction Section pages 236 – 237 for items marked with asterisk.

Page 183

Row 1:	#1-5	Shakers, ea.	5.00–6.00
	#6	Shaker or spice set in rotating tray	25.00–30.00
	#7	Tall yellow shaker	8.00–10.00
	#8	Amber shaker	10.00—12.50
	#9,10	Hocking opaque yellow, ea.	15.00–18.00
Row 2:	#1-16	Cattail, shakers ea.	3.00–4.00
Row 3:	#1,2	Delphite "basket wave" pr.	25.00–30.00
	#3	Delphite blue "Roman Arch" pepper	75.00–80.00
	#4	Sellers spice shaker	10.00–12.00
	#5	Hocking, crystal	3.00–4.00
	#6	Owens-Illinois green	7.50–8.00
	#7	Green, plain	6.00–7.00
	#8	Green, "Moisture Proof"	50.00–55.00
	#9,10	Jennyware, flat, pink, pr. w/labels	65.00–70.00

Row 3:	(Continued)		
	#11	Amber	12.50–15.00
Row 4:	#1,2	Hazel Atlas "Skating Dutch" flour or sugar	12.50–15.00
	#3,4	Hocking "Modern Tulips" salt or pepper	7.50–9.00
	#5-7	Roastmeat seasoning	30.00–35.00
		Same, salt or pepper	10.00–12.00
	#8,9	"Clambroth" white embossed salt or pepper	20.00–22.50
Row 5:	#1	Black pepper	15.00–20.00
	#2	Black sugar	20.00–25.00
	#3-6	Scotty dog salt or pepper	10.00–12.50
		Flour or sugar	15.00–17.50
	#7	Sitting bird pr.	15.00–20.00
	#8,9	Black flour or sugar	20.00–25.00

Hocking Glass Company (Rows 1-3)
Page 184

Row 1:	#1-4	Opaque yellow, ea.	15.00–18.00
	#5-7	Fired-on yellow, ea.	4.00– 6.00
	#8-10	Fired-on blue, ea.	10.00–12.00
Row 2:	#1	Fired-on green	7.00– 9.00
	#2, 3	Panelled fired-on blue, ea.	8.00–10.00
	#4-6	Green Clambroth, panelled, ea.	17.50–20.00
	#7, 8	Transparent green, ea.	10.00–12.00
	#9, 10	Vitrock, ea.	8.00–10.00
Row 3:	#1	Crystal w/raised dots	4.00– 5.00
	#2	Clambroth	8.00–10.00
	#3	Green, plain	9.00–11.00
	#4	Tulip (lid is valued at $1.00-2.00)	6.00– 8.00
	#5, 7 & 8	White, ea.	6.00– 8.00
	#6	Green Jad-ite	8.00–10.00
	#9	Green, round	20.00–25.00
Row 4:	#1, 2	Hazel Atlas embossed pink salt or pepper	*40.00–45.00
	#3	Same, crystal	20.00–25.00

Row 4:	(Continued)		
	#4, 5	Same, green salt or pepper	*30.00–35.00
	#6, 7	Same, flour or sugar	65.00–75.00
	#8	Dutch salt	12.50–15.00
	#9, 10	White w/green, ea.	10.00–12.00
Row 5:	#1-4	White w/black, ea.	10.00–12.00
	#5, 6	Black fired-on, ea.	8.00–10.00
	#7	Owens-Illinois ovoid shape (good lettering)	15.00–17.50
	#8, 9	Same, square shapes	8.50–10.00
	#10, 11	Sneath, amber, ea.	20.00–27.50
Row 6:	#1	Crystal, embossed celery	4.00– 5.00
	#2, 3	Crystal, embossed salt & sugar, ea.	5.00– 6.00
	#4	Green, embossed flour	35.00–40.00
	#5	Green	30.00–40.00
	#6	"Clambroth"	12.00–15.00
	#7	"Clambroth"	10.00–12.50
	#8	Black, round	17.50–20.00
	#9	Black	17.50–20.00
	#10	Black, ribbed	18.00–20.00

Page 185

Row 1:	#1, 2	Lady salt or pepper	20.00–22.50
	#3, 4	Same, flour or sugar	22.50–25.00
	#5, 6	Jadite, ea.	15.00–17.50
	#7, 8	"Art Deco," pr.	30.00–35.00
	#9, 10	Blue, pr.	18.00–22.00
	#11, 12	Fired-on blue, pr.	10.00–12.00
Row 2:	#1	Fired-on Dutch set	25.00–30.00
	#2	Dutch white set	15.00–17.50
	#3	Lady watering set (goes with Row 2 on previous page)	30.00–36.00
Row 3:	#1	Singing birds set	25.00–30.00

Row 3:	(Continued)		
	#2, 3	Scotty dogs, ea.	7.50– 9.00
	#4	Rooster set	10.00–12.50
	#5, 6	"Sombrero Sam" set	25.00–30.00
	#7, 8	White set w/salt dehumidifier	12.50–15.00
Row 4:	#1, 2	Black set (w/good lettering)	35.00–40.00
	#3, 4	Uncle Sam's hat set	10.00–12.50
	#5, 6	Vacuum cleaner attachments for blowing moth crystals, ea.	12.00–15.00
	#6-9	Floral or cherry, pr.	10.00–12.00

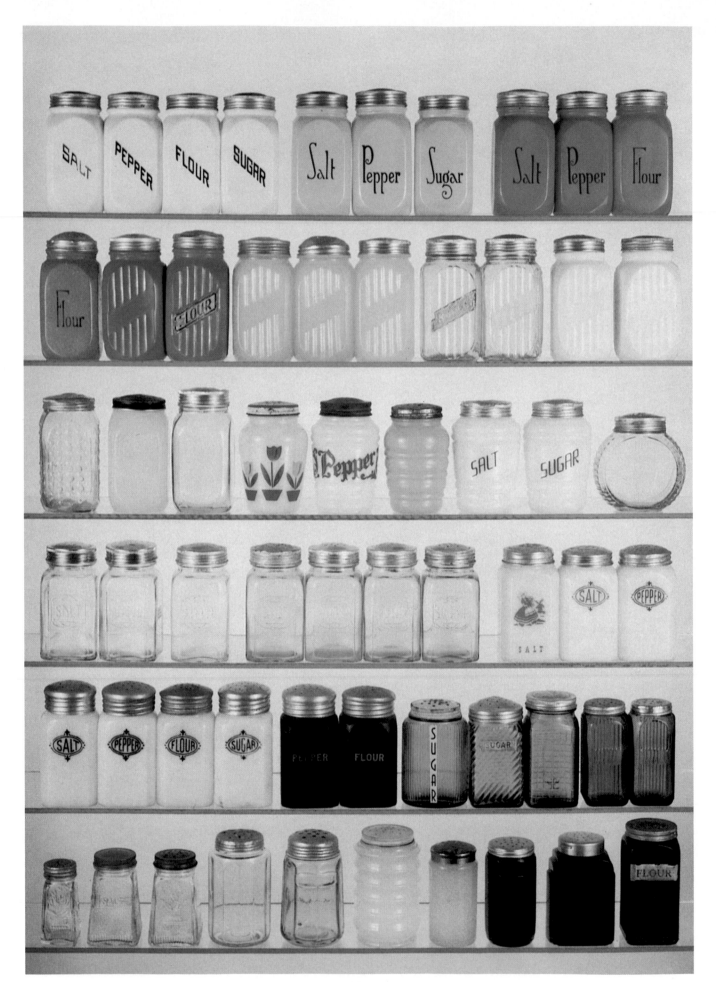

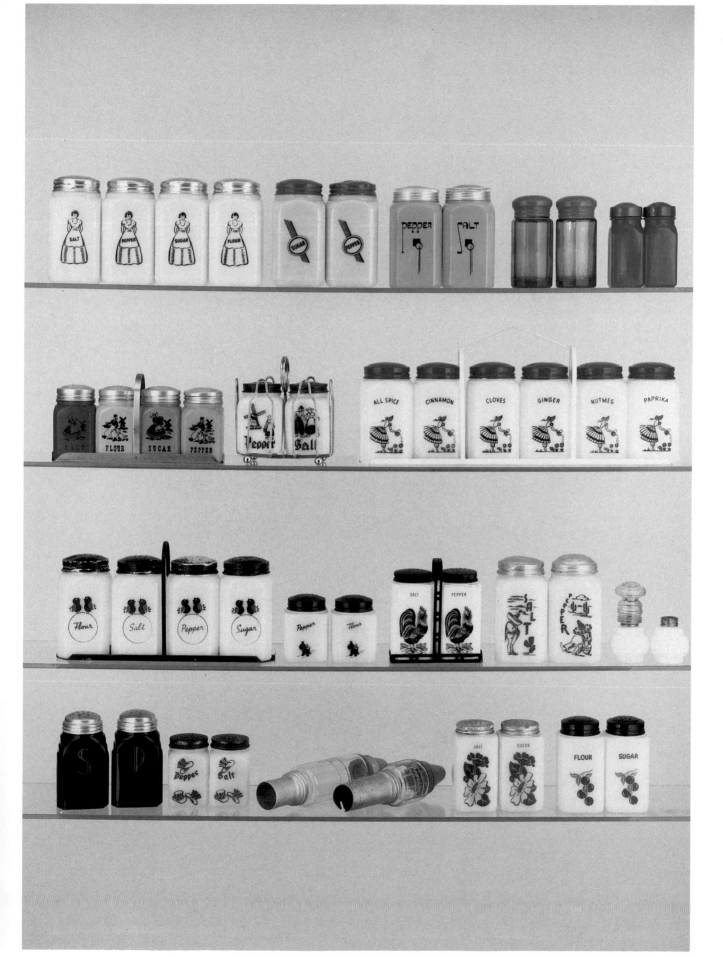

SHAKERS, Jeannette, McKee, etc.

All blue shakers are in demand, but there has also been an increase in demand for white and the later issued Fire King sets. New collectors start with the inexpensive sets and graduate to higher priced sets. Generally speaking, it would be better to buy the more expensive sets first! That is, if you can find them to buy!

Availability of all shakers has decreased in recent years. There are more salt and peppers found than other shakers, but one major problem with these heavily used items is worn lettering. Mint lettering on salt shakers is a premium! There were fewer flour, sugar, and spice sets made than salt and pepper sets. Possibly extra shakers came with grease sets and likely, ladies just did not buy shakers for flour and sugar!

Jeannette Glass Company (first 4½ rows)
Page 187

Row 1:	#1, 2	Delphite blue, 8 oz., salt or pepper, ea.	35.00– 40.00
	#3	Same, sugar	80.00– 90.00
	#4	Same, paprika	100.00–110.00
	#5, 6	Jadite, decorated salt/pepper, ea.	12.00– 15.00
	#7, 8	Same, mouth wash or bicarbonate soda	90.00–110.00
	#9, 10	Jadite, 6 oz. w/o label, ea.	6.00– 8.00
Row 2:	#1,2	Jadite light, salt or pepper	10.00– 12.00
	#3,4	Same, flour or sugar	12.00– 15.00
	#5	Jadite dark, pepper	9.00– 11.00
	#6	Same, flour	11.00– 13.00
	#7, 8	Delphite blue, square, salt or pepper	65.00– 75.00
	#9	Same, flour or sugar	75.00– 85.00
Row 3:	#1, 2	Jadite dark, square, salt or pepper	15.00– 17.50
	#3, 4	Same, flour or sugar	20.00– 22.50
	#5, 6	Jadite light, square, salt or pepper	15.00– 17.50

Row 3:	(Continued)		
	#7, 8	Same, flour or sugar	20.00–22.50
	#9	"Jennyware" pink	18.00–20.00
Row 4:	#1-4	"Jennyware" ultra-marine (subtract $1.00 missing label), ea.	22.00–25.00
	#5-8	Same, crystal	6.00– 8.00
Row 5:	#1-4	"Jennyware" flat shaker, pink, ea.	27.50–30.00
	#5	Same, crystal	18.00–20.00
	#6	Green, sold as sugar shaker	35.00–40.00
	#7	Unknown manufacturer, green "Zipper"	35.00–40.00
	#8	Crystal, "Zipper"	18.00–20.00
Row 6:	#1	Green, embossed flour	40.00–50.00
	#2	Crystal, embossed salt	18.00–20.00
	#3	Crystal, embossed allspice	18.00–20.00
	#4	Crystal, embossed cinnamon	18.00–20.00
	#5	Crystal, ribbed	10.00–12.00
	#6-11	Sneath green, ea.	40.00–50.00

McKee "Roman Arch" Shakers
Page 188

Row 1:	#1	Skokie green, salt	22.50–25.00
	#2-4	Same, pepper, flour or sugar	20.00–25.00
	#5	Same, cinnamon	35.00–38.00
	#6, 7	Delphite blue, salt or pepper	75.00–80.00
	#8-10	Fired-on colors, ea.	8.00–10.00
Row 2:	#1-9	"Dots," salt or pepper	15.00–17.50
	#1-9	Same, flour or sugar	22.50–25.00
	#10	Custard w/green flour	12.00–15.00
Row 3:	#1,2	Custard salt or pepper	10.00–12.00
	#3,4	Same, flour or sugar	12.00–15.00
	#5, 6	"Diamond Check," pr. on white	30.00–35.00
	#7, 8	"Dots" on white, pr.	20.00–24.00

Row 3:	(Continued)		
	#9, 10	Fired-on red, pr.	16.00–20.00
Row 4:	#1,2	White w/black, salt or pepper, ea.	12.00–15.00
	#3,4	Same, flour or sugar, ea.	20.00–22.00
	#5-7	White w/red, ea.	9.00–11.00
	#8, 9	Crystal, frosted, ea.	6.00– 7.00
Row 5:	#1-11	Black, pepper ($15.00-20.00) all others w/good lettering	20.00–25.00
		Black w/o lettering	6.00– 8.00
Row 6:	#1-4	Fired-on colored set	16.00–20.00
	#5	"Bow," red on white	10.00–12.00
	#6, 7	"Ships," salt or pepper	9.00–10.00
	#8, 9	Same, flour or sugar	10.00–12.00

McKee "Square" Shakers
Page 189

Row 1:	#1-3	Large, 16 oz., ea.	40.00– 45.00
	#4-7	Small, 8 oz., ea.	10.00– 12.00
	#8, 9	Skokie green, pr.	25.00– 30.00
Row 2:	#1, 2	Embossed dark jade salt or pepper	40.00– 45.00
	#3, 4	Same, flour or sugar	45.00– 50.00
	#5	Embossed Chalaine blue, ea.	100.00–125.00
	#6-9	Chalaine blue, ea.	75.00– 75.00
Row 3:	#1	White, salt, ea.	10.00– 12.00
	#2, 3	Flour or sugar, ea.	18.00– 20.00
	#4-8	"HOTPOINT" or "ELECTROCHEF" embossed white, ea.	8.00– 10.00
	#9, 10	White, ea.	9.00– 10.00
Row 4:	#1, 2, 5, 6	Skokie, green salt or pepper	15.00– 17.50
	#3, 4, 7	Same, flour or sugar	20.00– 22.50

Row 4:	(Continued)		
	#8	Same, "Cinnamon"	25.00–30.00
	#9, 10	Black w/o good lettering ($8.00-10.00) w/lettering, ea.	15.00–20.00
Row 5:	#1, 2	Custard, ea. salt or pepper	10.00–12.00
	#3, 4	Flour or sugar	17.50–20.00
	#5, 6	Same, ginger, cinnamon, nutmeg w/good lettering, ea.	25.00–30.00
	#8	Seville yellow, salt or pepper	12.00–15.00
	#9, 10	Same, flour or sugar	16.00–18.00
Row 6:	#1, 2	Seville yellow, salt or pepper	12.00–15.00
	#3, 4	Same, flour or sugar	16.00–18.00
	#5, 6	Skokie green, dark, salt or pepper, ea.	15.00–17.50
	#7, 8	Same, flour or sugar, ea.	20.00–22.50

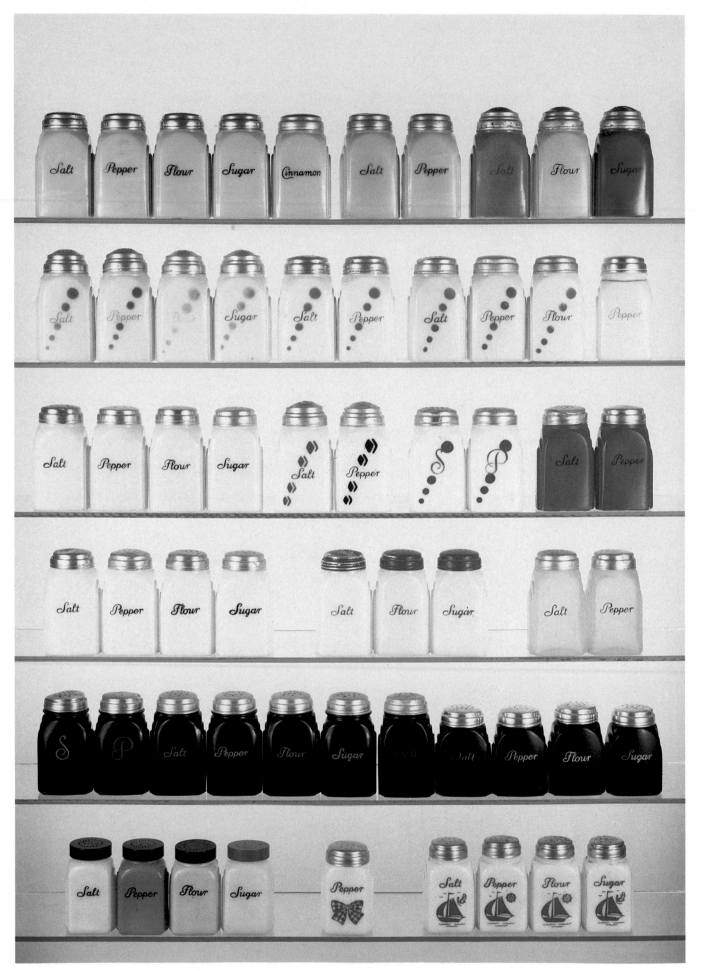

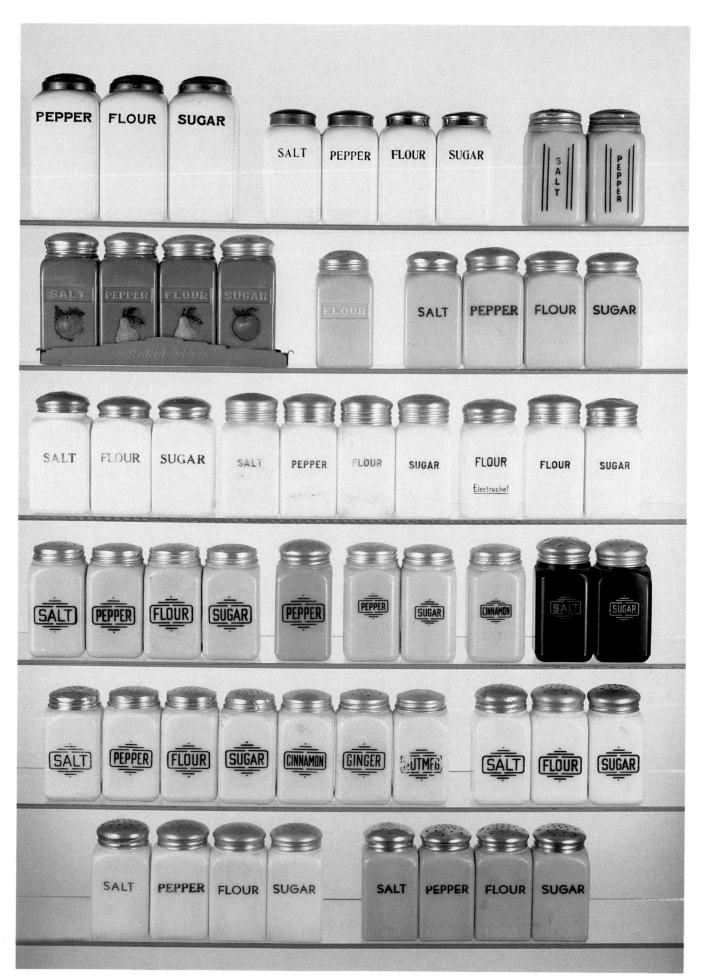

STRAW HOLDERS

Unfortunately, the biggest news on straw holders regards reproductions. Beware of any odd colored jars with a diamond design around the base. This design is similar to that on page 193, row 1, #2. These are being made in pink, an odd shade of green, and cobalt blue at the present. By the time you read this there may be additional colors. When you see a new metal insert — **beware** — it could be a newly made jar! As with any purchase, either know from whom you are buying, or if the price seems **too good to be true**, it usually is.

Collectors are still buying that Imperial pink vase to use as a straw jar. There has never been an **old** pink straw jar found. The straw jars shown on page 191 are out of a collection that I was able to borrow for this photograph. The pink straw jar (Imperial vase) shown in the last row is the same one pictured on page 192. Straw jars are among the items that can be found at antique advertising shows. Many collectors, today, have one of these "soda fountain" remembrances. We have one in our kitchen that had a lot of use when our kids were younger. They wouldn't drink a beverage without a straw!

Page 191

Row 1:	#1	Black	600.00–700.00
	#2	Green, tall	400.00–450.00
	#3	Green, short w/fancy metal base	400.00–450.00
	#4,5	Green, short, ea.	350.00–400.00
Row 2:	#1-4	Green, short, ea.	350.00–400.00
		(Some dealers ask a premium for jointed straw lifters)	
	#5	Pink, Imperial vase (used as straw jar, but is vase)	75.00–100.00

Page 192

Row 1:	#1	Cobalt blue, 12" (vase or straw jar?)	250.00–275.00
	#2, 3	Crystal Heisey w/top	225.00–275.00
	#4	Crystal Heisey "Greek Key" w/o lid (metal lid	125.00–150.00
		belongs page 193, Row 1, #2) w/glass lid	275.00–300.00
	#5	Pink, Imperial vase (used as straw jar, but is vase)	75.00–100.00
Row 2:	#1	Crystal, w/metal base	175.00–200.00
	#2	Crystal	75.00– 90.00
	#3	Green, short	350.00–400.00
	#4	Green, tall	400.00–450.00
	#5	Crystal, tall	110.00–150.00

Page 193

Row 1:	#1	Crystal, "Pattern Glass," zipper design, w/lid	225.00– 275.00
	#2	Crystal, w/metal base and lid (lid put on Greek	
		Key jar on page 180 by mistake)	125.00– 150.00
	#3	Emerald Green "Coca Cola"	1,000.00–1,200.00
	#4	Crystal knobbed lid (Candlewick collectors notice	
		this first)	150.00– 200.00
	#5	Crystal, "Pattern Glass," w/lid	250.00– 275.00
Row 2:	#1	Red, later made, possibly late 1950's/early 1960's	150.00– 200.00
	#2	Crystal, jointed straw lifter	100.00– 125.00
	#3	Crystal, named "Manhattan"	150.00– 200.00
	#4	Crystal, cut design on jar	100.00– 125.00
	#5	Crystal, zippered design, missing lid	75.00– 100.00
	#6	Amber, "English Hobnail," vase or straw jar	75.00– 85.00

191

SUGAR SHAKERS

The bullet shaped sugar shakers with indented dots near the top have been found with McKee papers.

Page 195

Row 1: #1, 2 Cambridge, #732, pink (ewer cream $35.00–40.00)   115.00–125.00
    #3, 4 Cambridge #732, green (tall ewer cream $35.00–40.00)   110.00–125.00
    #5   Cambridge, blue   150.00–160.00
    #6, 7 Cambridge, amber (syrup w/cover $45.00–50.00)   75.00– 85.00

Row 2: #1, 2 Cambridge, pink (ewer cream $25.00–30.00)   85.00– 95.00
    #3   Cambridge, amber, crystal foot & glass top   75.00– 90.00
    #4, 5 Same, pink (ewer cream $25.00–30.00)   100.00–110.00
    #6, 7 Heisey "Yeoman," pink (cream $25.00–30.00); (add $10.00–15.00 w/glass top)   75.00– 80.00
    #8   Cobalt blue   150.00–200.00
    #9   Green, w/green screw-in top   175.00–185.00

Row 3: #1, 2 Green or pink, footed ("Tilt-a-spoon")   235.00–250.00
    #3, 4 Green, 2 shades, possibly Paden City   150.00–165.00
    #5   Same, cobalt blue   600.00–650.00

Row 3: (Continued)
    #6   Same, amber   175.00–200.00
    #7   Paden City, pinched in, amber   150.00–175.00
    #8   Same, green   160.00–185.00

Row 4: #1   Green, Hocking   100.00–125.00
    #2   Green, Hocking   95.00–110.00
    #3   Unknown   50.00– 65.00
    #4   Green, "Hex Optic"   165.00–175.00
    #5   Amber   55.00– 65.00
    #6   Unknown, pink   80.00–100.00
    #7   Pink, w/red top   125.00–150.00
    #8   Paden City "Party Line," pink 85.00–100.00

Row 5: #1   Crystal, Paden City, 2 part dispenser   15.00– 18.00
    #2   Crystal, L.E. Smith   35.00– 40.00
    #3   Crystal, "West Sanitary Automatic Sugar"   20.00– 25.00
    #4, 5 Crystal, Hazel Atlas & unknown, ea.   10.00– 12.50
    #6   Crystal, faintly marked "Czechoslovakia"   20.00– 25.00

Page 196

Row 1: #1   Lancaster Glass Co., "Beehive," green   150.00–175.00
    #2-7 "Bullet" shape made by both Jeannette & Paden City
    #2, 3 Green   150.00–160.00
    #4   Yellow   200.00–250.00
    #5   Pink   175.00–200.00
    #6   Crystal   18.00– 25.00
    #7   Pink   175.00–200.00

Row 2: #1   Blue, "Monroe Mfg. Co., Elgin, Ill., Pat Pend." (liquid)   200.00–250.00
    #2   Same, pink   150.00–175.00
    #3, 4 Green or pink, footed   175.00–200.00
    #5   Green   150.00–175.00

Row 3: #1   Jeannette, light jade   55.00– 60.00
    #2-4 Same, pink decorated, green or yellowish jade, ea.   50.00– 60.00
    #5-7 Jeannette, pink or green   50.00– 60.00
    #6   Same, frosted pink   40.00– 50.00
    #8   Green, cone top   75.00– 85.00

Row 4: #1   White "Clambroth"   40.00– 45.00
    #2, 3 Green or pink   40.00– 45.00
    #4, 5 Orange or forest green   65.00– 75.00
    #6   Red   125.00–150.00
    #7   Amber, horseshoe pattern   35.00– 40.00
    #8   Green, older style   35.00– 45.00
    #9   Crystal, marked sugar & cinnamon   18.00– 20.00

Page 197

Row 1: #1   Yellow fired on w/red top   18.00 20.00
    #2   Crystal, McKee, indented dots at top   30.00– 40.00
    #3   Ultra-marine, Jeannette   225.00–250.00
    #4   Same, green   150.00–165.00
    #5   Cobalt blue   175.00–200.00
    #6   Crystal, cone top   25.00– 30.00
    #7   Fired-on red   18.00– 20.00

Row 2: #1   Amber   160.00–175.00
    #2   Pink   175.00–200.00
    #3   Black   250.00–300.00
    #4   Green   150.00–165.00
    #5   SCA (sun colored amethyst) 65.00– 75.00
    #6, 7 Hex Optic green or pink   165.00–175.00

Row 3: #1, 2 Heisey, pink or green   125.00–150.00
    #3   Same, crystal   50.00– 55.00
    #4   Green   100.00–115.00
    #5   Pink, measured teaspoon   150.00–165.00
    #6   Blue, marked "Made in Japan" (New!)   5.00– 10.00
    #7, 8 Pink or green   50.00– 65.00

Row 4: #1   Green   135.00–150.00

Row 4: (Continued)
    #2   Pink, Paden City "Rena" Line 154   175.00–200.00
    #3   Same, crystal   30.00– 35.00
    #4   Same, green   130.00–150.00
    #5   Amber   90.00–100.00
    #6   Blue   175.00–200.00
    #7   Amber   150.00–175.00

Row 5: #1   Pink, Jeannette   75.00– 85.00
    #2   Same, dark Jadite   60.00– 65.00
    #3   Green   60.00– 65.00
    #4   Forest green, Owens Illinois   15.00– 18.00
    #5   Green, individual sugar   50.00– 65.00
    #6   Same, amber   50.00– 55.00
    #7   Green, handled   75.00– 85.00

Row 6: #1   Crystal, decorated flowers   12.50– 15.00
    #2   Crystal "Rena" Line, Paden City   20.00– 22.00
    #3   Crystal, zippered design   15.00– 18.00
    #4, 8 Crystal, ea.   18.00– 20.00
    #5   Crystal, Fostoria "American"   45.00– 50.00
    #7   Crystal, "Beehive"   25.00– 30.00

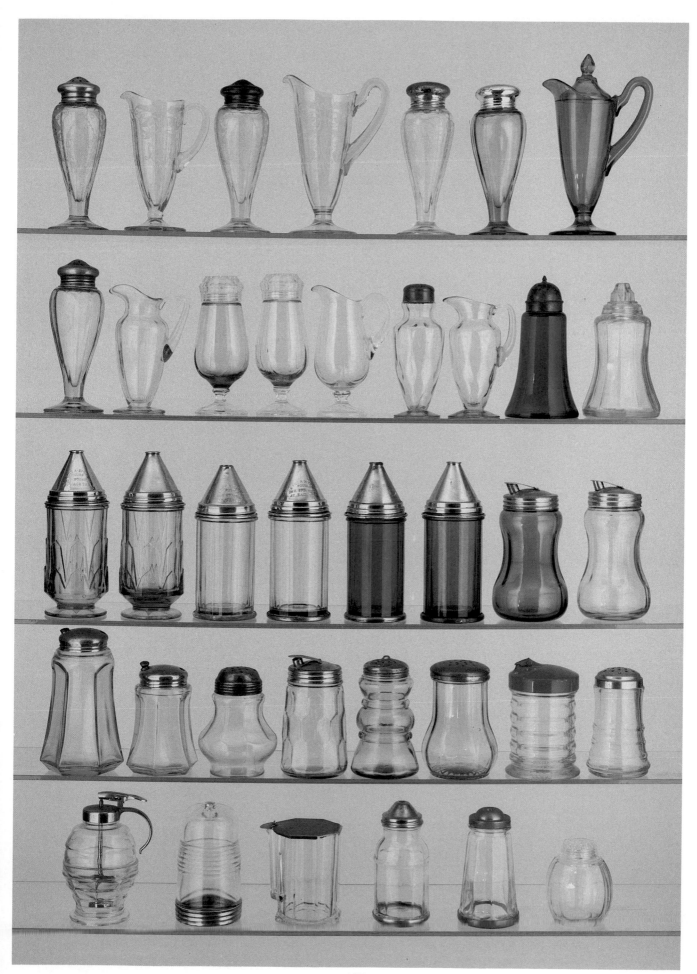

SYRUP PITCHERS

As with many of the other item collections, it is the major glass companies' syrup pitchers that are noticed first. The number of people I've encountered in my travels who collect syrup pitchers is phenomenal even to me. Somewhere during the conversation, they generally speak of attractive displays, fascinating shapes or colors. Generally, they carry pictures!

Row 1:	#1	Cambridge, w/cover, amber	45.00– 50.00
	#2	Same, green	60.00– 65.00
	#3	Paden City, green	30.00– 35.00
	#4	Imperial, w/slotted lid, pink	70.00– 75.00
	#5	Same, amber	65.00– 70.00
Row 2:	#1	Hazel Atlas, pink	45.00– 50.00
	#2	Same, green	25.00– 30.00
	#3	Same, pink	45.00– 50.00
	#4	Hazel Atlas, pink	45.00– 50.00
	#5	Hazel Atlas, green	40.00– 45.00
	#6	Same, pink	40.00– 45.00
Row 3:	#1, 2	Fostoria "Mayfair," green or pink w/underliner	55.00– 65.00
	#3	Fostoria "Chintz"	200.00–250.00
	#4	Fostoria, "Mayfair," yellow w/underliner	65.00– 70.00
	#5	Same, amber	50.00– 60.00
Row 4:	#1	Pink	40.00– 45.00
	#2	Green w/liner	40.00– 50.00
	#3	Imperial, pink	45.00– 50.00
	#4	Imperial, pink w/floral cutting	40.00– 45.00
	#5	Same, green, plain	40.00– 45.00
Row 5:	#1	Paden City #198, 8 oz., amber	40.00– 45.00
	#2	Same, green	35.00– 40.00
	#3	Same, pink	35.00– 40.00
	#4	Paden City "Party Line," green	35.00– 40.00
	#5	Same, pink	35.00– 40.00
	#6	Paden City #198, 12 oz. green w/liner	45.00– 50.00

SYRUP PITCHERS (Continued)

Row 1:	#1	Crystal	12.50– 15.00
	#2	Green (possibly U.S. Glass)	35.00– 40.00
	#3	Standard Glass, pink	35.00– 40.00
	#4	Hocking, green swirl	35.00– 40.00
	#5, 6	Crystal, ea.	10.00– 12.50
Row 2:	#1	Amber/yellow combination w/glass lid	40.00– 45.00
	#2	Pink w/green knob, handle & pink underliner	50.00– 55.00
	#3	Duncan & Miller "Caribbean," blue	150.00–175.00
	#4	Same, crystal	60.00– 75.00
	#5	Cambridge, amber	35.00– 40.00
Row 3:	#1	Paden City, green floral cutting w/underliner	35.00– 40.00
	#2	Same, pink	35.00– 40.00
	#3	Same, pink w/painted flowers	35.00– 40.00
	#4	Cambridge, pink	35.00– 40.00
	#5	Paden City, forest green	30.00– 35.00
Row 4:	#1, 3	Cambridge etched design w/underliner, pink	55.00– 65.00
	#2	Same, green	55.00– 65.00
	#4	Same, amber	45.00– 50.00
	#5	Cambridge, etched "Cleo"	150.00–175.00
Row 5:	#1	Cambridge, "Tally Ho" amber	40.00– 50.00
	#2	Cambridge, pink	50.00– 55.00
	#3	Same, amber	40.00– 50.00
	#4	Cambridge, amber	45.00– 50.00
	#5	Crystal, with crystal top	18.00– 20.00
	#6	Fenton, black	60.00– 75.00
Row 6:	#1	Heisey, "Moongleam" green	70.00– 75.00
	#2	Heisey, "Sahara" yellow	75.00– 85.00
	#3	Same, crystal	35.00– 40.00
	#4	Heisey, "Flamingo" pink	45.00– 50.00
	#5	Same, "Moongleam" green	50.00– 55.00
	#6	U.S. Glass miniature syrup, crystal	40.00– 45.00

WATER BOTTLES

There are many types of water containers shown throughout this book. People tend to think of plastic jugs as water containers today. Water bottles have gone the way of ice boxes which is where most of these were originally used.

The "RADIUM EMANATOR FILTER" bottle shown below is an interesting find. In its original McKee carton, there is an empty space where the radium filter was to have been placed. The set is made up of a 12" bottle (marked "Radium Emanator Filter Co., Inc., North Haledonn, N.J.") which turns up onto another 12½" bottle. The total filtering system stands 21" tall. The "Canary Yellow" color is called vaseline by collectors. This bottle set sells for $375.00–400.00.

Row 1:	#1	"Water Falls"	15.00–18.00
	#2	"Water"	10.00–12.00
	#3	"G.E." shows old refrigerator	15.00–18.00
	#4	"Well," amber	55.00–65.00
	#5	"Ships"	15.00–18.00
Row 2:	#1	Owen-Illinois "Juice" on one side & "Water" on other	6.00– 8.00
	#2	Forest green "Penguin"	15.00–18.00
	#3	Lattice design w/lid	45.00–50.00
	#4	Hocking "Royal Ruby"	75.00–85.00
	#5	"G.E." round	8.00–10.00
Row 3:	#1	"Crisscross," crystal	18.00–20.00
	#2	"The Well Informed Choose Ice Refrigeration"	8.00–10.00
	#3	"Beveragette," Pat. 1919	15.00–18.00
	#4	Cobalt blue, 64 oz., 10" tall	55.00–60.00
	#5	Same, 32 oz.	55.00–60.00

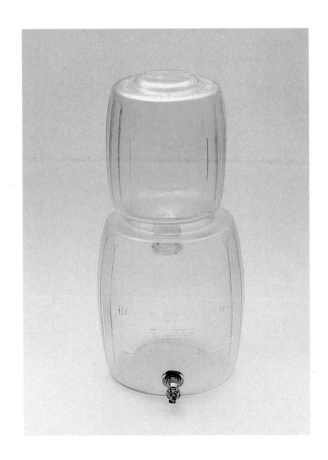

Part 3 – Patterns & Companies

"CRISSCROSS," Hazel Atlas Glass Company, 1936–1938

Collectors were first attracted to "Crisscross" because of the blue color. Now there are advocates for all colors including crystal. Crystal is often mixed with one of the other colors for a more varied appearance. Crystal prices have soared since the last book while the other colors have risen more slowly.

There are no new discoveries in this pattern, but the 5½" round bowl shown on page 207 is the piece presently eluding everyone. I have found a green lid, but no bottom.

Pink tumblers are elusive as are all colored sugars and creamers. No one has found a sugar and creamer in blue — yet. Nor have there been blue tumblers found to go with the pitchers. Those of you who collect other patterns of Depression era glass know how frustrating it is to collect a pattern that has a pitcher with no tumblers or vice versa.

Cobalt blue mixing bowls are just not being found! Many collectors are settling for bowls with use marks to have them at all. This has caused the prices for mint condition bowls to rise to the point that other collectors are settling for buying only the smaller mixing bowls and forgetting the two larger sizes.

One thing that confuses new collectors is the difference in the pound butter and the refrigerator dish that is like the butter. Look at the picture on page 207. The butter in Row 4 has a bottom that sticks out with tabs. The top of the refrigerator dish is flush with the edges of the bottom as seen in Row 3.

	Blue	Crystal	Green	Pink
Bottle, water, 32 oz.	—	18.00– 20.00	90.00–100.00	—
Bottle, water, 64 oz.	—	22.00– 25.00	100.00–125.00	—
Bowl, mixing set (5)	240.00–270.00	55.00– 67.00	115.00–135.00	115.00–130.00
Bowl, mixing, 6⅝"	20.00– 30.00	6.00– 8.00	15.00– 18.00	12.00– 15.00
Bowl, mixing, 7⅝"	35.00– 40.00	8.00– 10.00	18.00– 20.00	18.00– 20.00
Bowl, mixing, 8¾"	45.00– 50.00	10.00– 12.00	22.00– 25.00	22.00– 25.00
Bowl, mixing, 9⅝"	55.00– 60.00	12.00– 15.00	25.00– 30.00	28.00– 30.00
Bowl, mixing, 10⅝"	85.00– 90.00	20.00– 22.00	35.00– 40.00	35.00– 40.00
Butter, ¼ lb.	85.00– 95.00	15.00– 18.00	35.00– 40.00	35.00– 40.00
Butter, 1 lb.	85.00– 95.00	18.00– 20.00	35.00– 40.00	35.00– 40.00
Creamer	—	12.00– 15.00	35.00– 40.00	35.00– 40.00
Food mixer (baby face)	—	30.00– 35.00	—	—
Pitcher, 54 oz.	600.00–700.00	100.00–110.00	—	—
Reamer, lemon	—	10.00– 12.00	20.00– 22.00	275.00–300.00
Reamer, orange	250.00–275.00	10.00– 12.00	20.00– 22.00	200.00–225.00
Refrigerator bowl, round 5½" w/cover	125.00–150.00	12.00– 15.00	120.00–135.00	125.00–140.00
Refrigerator bowl, w/cover				
4" x 4"	25.00– 30.00	6.00– 8.00	20.00– 22.00	18.00– 20.00
4" x 8"	75.00– 80.00	12.00– 15.00	30.00– 33.00	28.00– 30.00
8" x 8"	100.00–110.00	15.00– 18.00	35.00– 40.00	40.00– 45.00
Refrigerator dish (like butter),				
3½" x 5¾"	90.00–100.00	18.00– 20.00	45.00– 50.00	—
Sugar	—	12.50– 15.00	25.00– 28.00	25.00– 30.00
Sugar lid	—	20.00– 25.00	40.00– 45.00	35.00– 40.00
Tumbler, 9 oz.	—	25.00– 30.00	—	75.00– 85.00

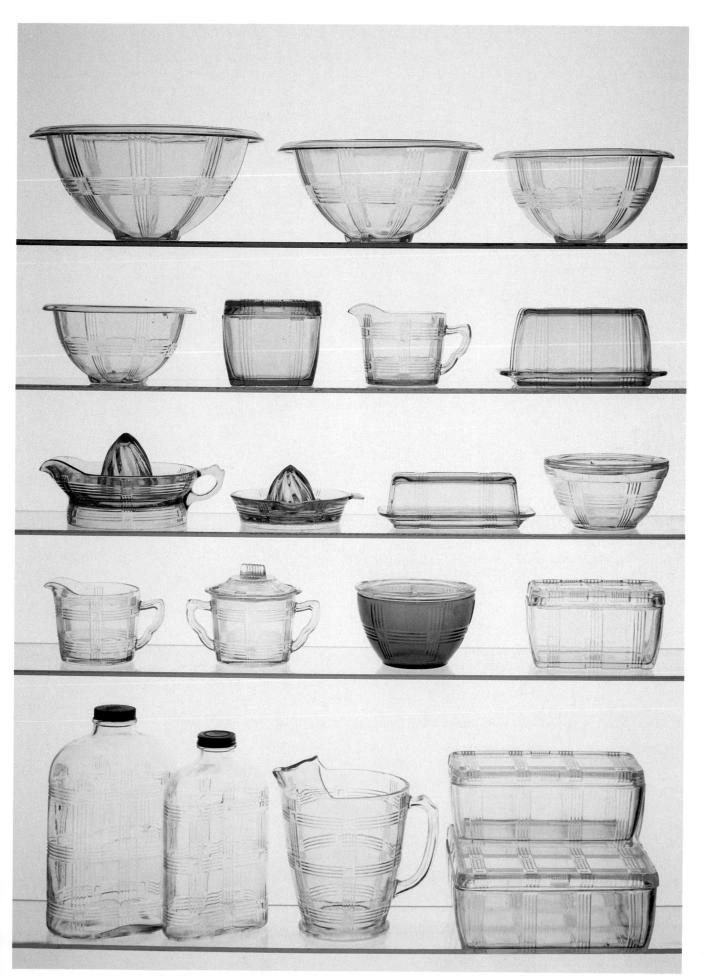

"DOTS," McKee Glass Company, 1930's – Early 1940's

McKee issued this as a "Deluxe" line of kitchenware and sold items to merchants from $4.00–12.00 per dozen. I have priced most items available although only a representative sampling can be seen on pages 209 and 211.

Page 209	Black/Green Dots on Custard	Blue/Red Dots on Custard	Dots on White
Bowl, 9", scalloped edge	30.00– 35.00	30.00– 35.00	22.00–25.00
Bowl, 9", w/spout	22.50– 25.00	25.00– 28.00	20.00–22.00
Bowl, drippings	30.00– 33.00	30.00– 35.00	20.00–22.50
Bowl, egg beater w/lip	20.00– 25.00	22.50– 25.00	15.00–17.50
Butter dish, 1 pound	100.00–125.00	100.00–125.00	45.00–50.00
Canister, 48 oz., screw lid	60.00– 65.00	65.00– 75.00	45.00–50.00
Canister, 28 oz., screw lid	45.00– 50.00	45.00– 50.00	35.00–40.00
Canister & lid, round, 48 oz.	22.50– 25.00	25.00– 28.00	20.00–22.00
Canister & lid, round, 40 oz.	20.00– 22.50	22.50– 25.00	18.00–20.00
Canister & lid, round, 24 oz.	18.00– 20.00	18.00– 20.00	12.00–15.00
Canister & lid, round, 10 oz.	15.00– 18.00	16.00– 18.00	12.00–15.00
Mixing bowl, 9"	16.00– 18.00	17.50– 20.00	12.50–15.00
Mixing bowl, 8"	15.00– 17.50	15.00– 17.50	12.00–15.00
Mixing bowl, 7"	12.00– 15.00	12.00– 15.00	10.00–12.00
Mixing bowl, 6"	10.00– 12.00	10.00– 12.50	8.00–10.00
Pitcher, 2 cup	35.00– 38.00	35.00– 38.00	25.00–28.00
Refrigerator dish, 4" x 5"	15.00– 18.00	15.00– 18.00	8.00–10.00
Refrigerator dish, 5" x 8"	20.00– 22.50	20.00– 25.00	15.00–18.00
Shaker, salt or pepper, ea.	15.00– 17.50	15.00– 17.50	12.00–15.00
Shaker, flour or sugar, ea.	22.50– 25.00	22.50– 25.00	18.00–20.00

"DOTS," Hazel Atlas & Hocking Glass Companies '30's – '50's

Dot designed kitchenware was made by several companies. The later made Fire-King "Dots" can be found in red, gold and black. These Dot designs are becoming very popular patterns with collectors, although red "Dots" seems the more coveted color. It's been dubbed "Measles" by collectors!

Page 210

Row 1:	#1	Hazel Atlas bowl, 9", red	18.00–20.00
	#2	Same, 8"	15.00–18.00
	#3	Hazel Atlas pitcher, 2 cup	30.00–35.00
	#4	Pitcher, ribbed 2 cup	22.50–25.00
Row 2:	#1	Hazel Atlas bowl, 8", yellow	12.00–15.00
	#2	Same, 6"	8.00–10.00
		Same, 7" (not shown)	10.00–12.00
	#3	Red, 5"	8.00–10.00
	#4	Hocking grease jar	15.00–18.00

Row 3:	#1	Hocking red bowl, 9½"	12.00–15.00
		Same, 8½" (not shown)	10.00–12.00
	#2	Same, 7½"	8.00–10.00
	#3	Same, 6½"	5.00– 6.00
Row 4:	#1	Hocking "Apple," 9½"	12.00–15.00
		Same, 8½" (not shown)	10.00–12.00
		Same, 7½" (not shown)	8.00–10.00
	#2	Same, 6½"	5.00– 6.00

FIRE-KING Anchor Hocking Glass Company, Late 40'S – 60's

An assortment of Dots is shown here along with Anchor Hocking's popular "Tulips" design. Grease jars and the designed "Tulips" shaker tops (without rust and damage) are becoming scarce.

Page 211

Row 1:	#1	McKee refrigerator dish, 4" x 5"	15.00–18.00
	#2	McKee 24 oz. round canister w/lid	18.00–20.00
	#3	Anchor Hocking 7½" gold "Dots" bowl	8.00–10.00
Row 2:	#1	Red "Dots" 8" bowl	12.00–15.00
	#2	Yellow "Dots" 6" bowl	6.00–8.00
	#3	Brown "Dots" 5" bowl	5.00–6.00
Row 3:	#1	"Banded Dots" 8½" blue bowl	12.00–15.00
	#2	Same, 7" yellow bowl	8.00–10.00

Row 3:	(Continued)		
	#3	Pyrex "Art Deco" casserole	75.00–100.00
Row 4:	#1	"Tulips" bowl, 9½"	12.00–15.00
	#2	Same, 8½"	10.00–12.00
	#3	Same, 7½"	8.00–10.00
Row 5:	#1	Same, 6½"	6.00– 8.00
	#2	Same, grease jar	18.00–20.00
	#3	Same, shaker	6.00– 7.50
	#4	Batter bowl, "Fruits" (peaches, grapes and pears)	17.50–20.00

209

FIRE-KING

Page 213

Row 1: #1   Pink Floral, casserole, 1 qt.   10.00–12.00
    #2   Same, 4" refrigerator dish   3.00– 4.00
    #3   Same, 8" bowl   10.00–12.00
    #4   Same, 5 oz. low custard   2.50– 3.00
    #5   Fruit, 5 oz. low custard   2.50– 3.00
    #6   Fruit, 8 oz. mug   6.00– 8.00
Row 2: #1   "Splash Proof," "Turquoise Blue,"
      9½" mixing bowl, 4 qt.   12.50–15.00
      Same, 8½", 3 qt. (not shown)   10.00–12.00
    #2   Same, 7½", 2 qt.   8.00–10.00
    #3   Same, 6½", 1 qt.,   8.00–10.00
    #4   7½" gold "Dots" bowl   8.00–10.00
Row 3: #1   "Swedish Modern," "Turquoise Blue,"
      11" mixing bowl, 3 qt.   18.00–20.00

Row 3: (Continued)
    #2   Same, 9½", 2 qt.   15.00–17.50
    #3   Same, 8", 1 qt.   12.50–15.00
    #4   Same, 6½", 1 pt.   10.00–12.00
Row 4: #1   "Ivory," 9" cake pan   12.00–14.00
    #2   Same, 9⅛" deep loaf pan   10.00–12.00
    #3   Same, 10½" baking pan   12.00–15.00
Row 5: #1   Silver decorated casserole,
      signed "Georges Briard"   20.00–25.00
    #2   Pedestal Ivory cake plate   6.00– 8.00
    #3   Forest Green batter bowl   10.00–12.50
    #4   Forest Green, 6½", 1 qt. bowl   7.00– 8.00

Page 214

Row 1: #1   "Modern Tulip" 3 qt.
      mixing bowl   10.00–12.00
    #2   Same, 4 qt.   12.00–15.00
    #3   Same, 2 qt.   8.00–10.00
    #4   Same, 1 qt.   6.00– 8.00
Row 2: #1,3   "Modern Tulip" salt and
      pepper pr.   12.00–15.00
    #2,5   "Modern Tulip" or Apples
      and Cherries grease jar   18.00–20.00
    #4   "Kitchen Aids" 2 qt. mixing bowl   8.00–10.00
Row 3: #1   Fleur-de-lis Leaf, bowl, 7"   6.00– 7.00
    #2   Same, 6"   5.00– 6.00

Row 3: (Continued)
    #3   Same, 5"   4.00– 5.00
    #4,5   Grecian scene tumbler
      (showing front and back), ea.   6.00– 7.50
    #6   Same, ice bowl   10.00–12.00
Row 4: #1   Souvenir mug, Patton Museum,
      Ft. Knox, Ky.   6.00– 8.00
    #2-5   Water Lily sherbet, ea.   2.00– 3.00
    #6   Esso "Tony the Tiger" mug   6.00– 8.00
Row 5: #1   Basket weave 4" bowl   1.50– 2.00
    #2   Chicken and Fruit, 1 qt. casserole   4.00– 5.00
    #3   Same, 2 qt.   6.00– 7.00

FIRE-KING, Sapphire Blue

Page 215

Baker, 1 pt., round or square	5.00– 6.00	Cup, 8 oz measuring, 3 spout	18.00–20.00
Baker, 1 qt.	8.00– 10.00	Custard cup, 5 oz.	2.00– 3.00
Baker, 1½ qt.	10.00– 12.00	Custard cup, 6 oz., 2 styles	2.50– 3.50
Baker, 2 qt.	12.00– 15.00	Loaf pan, 9⅛", deep	18.00–20.00
Bowl, 5⅜", cereal or deep dish		Nurser, 4 oz.	12.00–15.00
pie plate	12.00– 15.00	Nurser, 8 oz.	22.50–25.00
Bowl, 4⅜", individual pie plate	12.00– 15.00	Pie plate, 8⅜"	7.00– 8.00
Bowl, 16 oz. measuring, 2 spout	22.00– 25.00	Pie plate, 9"	8.00– 9.00
Cake pan (deep), 8¾"	20.00– 22.00	Pie plate, 9⅝"	8.00–10.00
Casserole, 1 pt., knob handle cover	12.00– 15.00	Pie plate, 10⅜", w/juice saver rim	75.00–80.00
Same, 1 qt.	12.00– 15.00	Percolator top, 2⅛"	3.50– 5.00
Same, 1½ qt.	12.00– 15.00	Refrigerator jar & cover, 4½" x 5"	10.00–12.00
Same, 2 qt.	18.00– 20.00	Same, 5⅛" x 9⅛"	25.00–30.00
Casserole, individual, 10 oz.	10.00– 12.00	Roaster, 8¾"	40.00–45.00
Casserole, 1 qt., pie plate cover	15.00– 18.00	Roaster, 10⅜"	60.00–65.00
Same, 1½ qt.	15.00– 18.00	Table server, tab handles (hot plate)	15.00–18.00
Same, 2 qt.	18.00– 20.00	Utility bowl, 6⅞"	10.00–12.00
Coffee mug, 7 oz., 2 styles	22.00– 25.00	Utility bowl, 8⅜"	12.00–15.00
Cup, 8 oz., dry measure, no spout	200.00–250.00	Utility bowl, 10⅛"	15.00–18.00
Cup, 8 oz. measuring, 1 spout	15.00– 18.00	Utility pan, 8⅛" x 12½"	20.00–22.00

MIXING BOWLS

	PACKING
G4100/1 —4 Pce. Mixing Bowl Set	6 sets — 41 lbs.
(Each Set in Gift Carton)	
G4100/54 —4 Pce. Mixing Bowl Set	2 doz. —140 lbs.
(Bulk Packed in 6 Cartons)	sets
G4100/66 —4 Pce. Mixing Bowl Set	8 sets — 48 lbs.
(Each Set Nested & Packed in an Individual Cell)	

The Sets listed above consist of one each of the G4156, G4157, G4158 and G4159 Bowls.

OPEN STOCK

G4156—6" Mixing Bowl	2 doz. — 18 lbs.
G4157—7" Mixing Bowl	2 doz. — 26 lbs.
G4158—8" Mixing Bowl	1 doz. — 20 lbs.
G4159—9" Mixing Bowl	1 doz. — 28 lbs.

	PACKING
G300/129—3 Pce. Mixing Bowl Set	2 doz. — 68 lbs.
(Bulk Packed in 3 Cartons)	sets
COMPOSITION: One each 4 7/8", 6" and 7 1/4" Bowls	

OPEN STOCK

G355—4 7/8" Mixing Bowl	2 doz. — 13 lbs.
G356—6" Mixing Bowl	2 doz. — 21 lbs.
G357—7 1/4" Mixing Bowl	2 doz. — 34 lbs.

"MODERN TULIP" DECORATION

RANGE SET

W300/244—4 Pce. Range Set
  Each Set in Gift Carton, 8 Sets to Shipping Carton — 19 lbs.
COMPOSITION: One Salt Shaker—White Top
    One Pepper Shaker—White Top
    One Range Jar & Cover

The above Range Set and matching Mixing Bowl Sets in "Modern Tulip" decoration, are not available in Open Stock.

W300/242—3 Pce. Mixing Bowl Set
  Each Set Nested & Packed in an Individual Cell,
  8 Sets to Shipping Carton — 44 lbs.
COMPOSITION: One 1 Qt. Mixing Bowl
    One 2 Qt. Mixing Bowl
    One 3 Qt. Mixing Bowl

W300/243—4 Pce. Mixing Bowl Set
  Each Set in Gift Carton, 4 Sets to Shipping Carton — 37 lbs.
COMPOSITION: One 1 Qt. Mixing Bowl
    One 2 Qt. Mixing Bowl
    One 3 Qt. Mixing Bowl
    One 4 Qt. Mixing Bowl

HEAT-PROOF

MIXING BOWLS

PACKING

W4100/5 —4 Pce. Mixing Bowl Set .... 6 sets — 41 lbs.
    (Each Set in Gift Carton)

W4100/55—4 Pce. Mixing Bowl Set .... 2 doz. —150 lbs.
    (Bulk Packed in 6 Cartons)   sets

W4100/67—4 Pce. Mixing Bowl Set .... 8 sets — 48 lbs.
    (Each Set Nested & Packed in an Individual Cell)

The Sets listed above consist of one each of the
W4156, W4157, W4158 and W4159 Bowls

OPEN STOCK

W4156—6" Mixing Bowl .... 2 doz. — 19 lbs.
W4157—7" Mixing Bowl .... 2 doz. — 29 lbs.
W4158—8" Mixing Bowl .... 1 doz. — 22 lbs.
W4159—9" Mixing Bowl .... 1 doz. — 29 lbs.

PACKING

W300/130—3 Pce. Mixing Bowl Set .... 2 doz. — 66 lbs.
    (Bulk Packed in 3 Cartons)   sets
COMPOSITION: One each 4 7/8", 6" and 7 1/4" Bowls

OPEN STOCK

W355—4 7/8" Mixing Bowl .... 2 doz. — 13 lbs.
W356—6" Mixing Bowl .... 2 doz. — 20 lbs.
W357—7 1/4" Mixing Bowl .... 2 doz. — 33 lbs.
W358—8 3/8" Mixing Bowl (Not Illustrated) ... 1 doz. — 27 lbs.

"KITCHEN AIDS" DECORATION

RANGE SET

W300/239—4 Pce. Range Set
    Each Set in Gift Carton, 8 Sets to Shipping Carton — 19 lbs.
COMPOSITION: One Salt Shaker—White Top
                One Pepper Shaker—White Top
                One Range Jar & Cover

The above Range Set and matching Mixing Bowl
Sets in "Kitchen Aids" decoration, are not
available in Open Stock.

W300/237—3 Pce. Mixing Bowl Set
    Each Set Nested & Packed in an Individual Cell,
    8 Sets to Shipping Carton — 44 lbs.
COMPOSITION: One 1 Qt. Mixing Bowl
                One 2 Qt. Mixing Bowl
                One 3 Qt. Mixing Bowl

W300/238—4 Pce. Mixing Bowl Set
    Each Set in Gift Carton, 4 Sets to Shipping Carton — 37 lbs.
COMPOSITION: One 1 Qt. Mixing Bowl
                One 2 Qt. Mixing Bowl
                One 3 Qt. Mixing Bowl
                One 4 Qt. Mixing Bowl

HEAT-PROOF

FRY GLASSWARE, H.C. Fry Glass Company, 1920's–1930's

The opalescent white color most people are familiar with was called "Pearl" by the factory. Decorated pieces are more desirable than the regular issues. All colors are rarer than the "Pearl" with both blue shades ("Azure" {light} and "Royal" {cobalt}) the most in demand. Fry glass without an opalescent effect is called "lime glass." According to avid Fry collectors, ovenware condition is not as important as obtaining an important addition to a collection.

All dates or numbers listed are marked on the piece.

Page 219

Row 1:	#1	Reamer, fluted, jello mold, "Canary"	250.00–	275.00
	#2	Meat loaf w/lid, rectangular, 9"	50.00–	55.00
	#3	Reamer, straight side	300.00–	325.00
Row 2:	#1	Grill plate, 8½", "Rose"	25.00–	30.00
	#2	Same, "Azure" blue	30.00–	40.00
	#3	Measure cup, 3 spout, "Pearl"	65.00–	75.00
	#4	Bean pot w/lid, 1 pt.	45.00–	50.00
Row 3:	#1	Grill plate, 10½", "Rose"	40.00–	45.00
	#2	Measure cup, 1 spout	50.00–	60.00
	#3	Grill plate, 10½", "Pearl" w/blue trim	50.00–	65.00
Row 4:	#1	Same, w/orange enamel trim	50.00–	65.00
	#2	Reamer, straight side, "Azure" blue	1,500.00–	1,600.00

Row 4:		(Continued)		
	#3	Same as #1, "Royal" blue	50.00–	65.00
Row 5:	#1	Meat platter, 13", green, "Not Heat Resisting Glass"	70.00–	80.00
	#2	Percolator top w/blue finial	20.00–	25.00
	#3	Snack plate, 6" x 9", w/cup "Royal" blue	50.00–	60.00
Row 6:	#1	Same as Row 5 #1, 17"	85.00–	100.00
	#2	Percolator top w/green finial	18.00–	20.00
	#3	Casserole, oval, 7", w/green trim	45.00–	50.00

Page 220

Row 1:	#1	Domed roaster (1946-14) 14" x 10" x 7½"	150.00–	165.00
	#2	Same as #1 but in metal holder. Paper label reads: "This is a 'ROYALLOY' Steel Frame. Dry thoroughly after using and it will serve you well and long."	160.00–	175.00

Row 2: Sunnybrook Cookie Jar
(Introduced at $0.57; original price $0.75)

#1	"Royal" blue	250.00–	275.00
#2	Green	175.00–	225.00
#3	"Rose"	175.00–	200.00
#4	Black	250.00–	275.00

Page 221

Row 1:	#1	Bean pot w/lid, 1 qt. in holder	55.00–65.00
	#2	Cream soup, 5¼", ftd.	45.00–50.00
	#3	Casserole w/lid, 8" round, in holder	20.00–30.00
Row 2:	#1	Casserole, oval, 10" w/green finial	60.00–70.00
	#2	Sundae glass "MACO-MFG-CO, VAPOR-RITE, MAY-WOOD-ILL	50.00–55.00
	#3	Oval platter, 9" x 13"	35.00–40.00
Row 3:	#1	Casserole, 6" round	20.00–25.00
	#2	Baker, 6" round	20.00–22.00
	#3	Cocotte, 5" (for indiv. meat, chicken, oyster pies)	12.00–15.00
	#4	Same, 4"	12.00–15.00
	#5	Custard cup, 4½ oz.	5.00–8.00
Row 4:	#1	Snack plate, 6" x 9" w/cup	25.00–30.00
	#2	Mushroom baker/round shirred egg, 6"	75.00–100.00

Row 4:		(Continued)	
	#3	Baker, oval, 6"	20.00–25.00
	#4	Apple baker or custard, 4¾"	15.00–18.00
Row 5:	#1	Butter pat (?) "Fry's Heat Resisting Glass"	50.00–75.00
	#2	Ramekin, 3"	8.00–10.00
	#3, 4 & 7	Custard cup, 4 or 6 oz. (1927 or 1936)	8.00–10.00
	#5, 6	Custard cup, 6 oz., engraved (1927 or 1936)	10.00–12.00
Row 6:	#1	Casserole, 7" round, engraved w/blue finial	70.00–80.00
	#2, 3	Ramekin "Pearl" or "Lime glass," ea.	8.00–10.00
	#4	Oval server, 8 sided, engraved, 6½" x 9"/holder	60.00–65.00

FRY GLASSWARE, H.C. Fry Glass Company 1920's–1930's (Continued)

The antique business is a conduit to meeting many interesting collectors from all over the country. At the Heisey Convention in 1988, I met a couple of avid Fry collectors on preview night. I would like to thank Hank and Carla Bowman for the use of their Fry glassware for this section as well as for providing valuable information for use in the book. Hopefully, I will be able to go back to California for photographs for the next book.

Most people in all collecting fields are more than willing to share glass and information. That is one of the more rewarding aspects of writing. I hope you gain knowledge to help your collecting from the long hours spent compiling this.

Row 5 consists of a child's set that was sold for $2.50 in 1922. It was called "Little Mother's Kidibake Set" and now sells for $300.00.

Page 223

Row 1:	#1	Casserole w/lid, 7" square, in holder	45.00–55.00
	#2	Baker, pudding, 2⅛" x 6⅜"	18.00–20.00
	#3	Casserole w/lid, 8" oval, engraved in holder	40.00–45.00
Row 2:	#1	Brown betty, 9"	50.00–55.00
	#2	Casserole w/lid, 7" round, engraved side & lid	50.00–55.00
		Trivet, 8" under casserole	15.00–17.50
	#3	Shirred egg, 7½", round	20.00–25.00
Row 3:	#1	Vegetable dish, 2 part, 9¾"	30.00–35.00
	#2	Fish platter, 11", engraved	45.00–55.00
	#3	Pie plate, 9½", engraved, in holder	30.00–35.00
Row 4:	#1	Cake, 9" round	20.00–22.50
	#2	Cup and saucer, No. 1969	40.00–45.00
	#3	Pie plate, 10" in metal holder	20.00–25.00
Row 5:	#1	Pie plate, 5"	50.00–60.00
	#2	Casserole w/lid, 4½" round	75.00–85.00
	#3,4	Ramekin, 2½", ea	30.00–40.00
	#5	Bread baker, 5"	55.00–70.00
Row 6:	#1	Fish platter, 17", engraved	50.00–60.00
	#2	Casserole w/lid, 7" round, embossed w/grapes	55.00–65.00

"JENNYWARE," Jeannette Glass Company, 1936-1938

"Jennyware" is popular with collectors due, in part, to the many different items that can be acquired. A major problem in collecting "Jennyware" is the variations of color occurring in ultra-marine. The greenish shade of "Jennyware" has few collectors. Dealers usually avoid buying that shade for resale.

That decanter in the top row was made by Imperial and is not a part of the "Jennyware" set. Many collectors buy it as a "go-with" item. It sells for $40.00-50.00.

Page 225, 226

	Crystal	Pink	Ultra-marine
Bowl, mixing set (3)	38.00– 45.00	85.00– 95.00	90.00–105.00
Bowl, 10½"	18.00– 20.00	35.00– 40.00	35.00– 45.00
Bowl, 8¼"	12.00– 15.00	25.00– 30.00	35.00– 37.50
Bowl, 6"	8.00– 10.00	22.50– 25.00	20.00– 22.50
Butter dish, deep bottom	50.00– 60.00	110.00–125.00	125.00–150.00
Butter dish, flat bottom	—	—	200.00–250.00
Coaster	—	6.00– 8.00	6.00– 8.00
Measuring cup set (4)	90.00–110.00	140.00–160.00	150.00–170.00
1 cup	30.00– 35.00	45.00– 50.00	50.00– 55.00
½ cup	25.00– 30.00	40.00– 45.00	40.00– 45.00
⅓ cup	20.00– 25.00	30.00– 35.00	35.00– 40.00
¼ cup	15.00– 20.00	25.00– 30.00	25.00– 30.00
Pitcher, 36 oz.	50.00– 55.00	80.00– 90.00	100.00–110.00
Reamer	75.00– 85.00	90.00–100.00	100.00–110.00
Refrigerator dish, 70 oz., round	20.00– 25.00	50.00– 55.00	50.00– 55.00
Refrigerator dish, 32 oz., round	18.00– 20.00	30.00– 35.00	30.00– 35.00
Refrigerator dish, 16 oz., round	12.00– 15.00	27.50– 30.00	25.00– 30.00
Refrigerator dish, 4½" x 4½"	12.00– 15.00	22.00– 25.00	22.00– 25.00
Refrigerator dish, 4½" x 9"	18.00– 20.00	30.00– 32.50	30.00– 32.50
Shaker, footed, ea.	6.00– 8.00	18.00– 20.00	22.00– 25.00
Shaker, flat, ea.	18.00– 20.00	27.50– 30.00	—
Tumbler, 8 oz.	20.00– 22.00	30.00– 35.00	40.00– 45.00

Pyrex, Corning Glass Works

Delphite blue Corning glassware is beginning to attract more American collectors. Canadian collectors have been aware of it for years.

Page 227

Row 1:	#1	Blue 12" Pyrex, square based bowl	20.00– 25.00
	#2	Blue 10" pie plate	18.00– 20.00
	#3	Blue divided relish	20.00– 22.50
Row 2:	#1	Crystal Pyrex measure cup	12.50– 15.00
	#2	Pyrex "Clambroth" white oval casserole	100.00–125.00
	#3	Pyrex red refrigerator dish	100.00–125.00
Row 3:	#1	Mixing bowl , 8½"	12.00– 14.00
	#2	Mixing bowl , 7½"	10.00– 12.00
	#3	Mixing bowl , 6½"	8.00– 9.00
Row 4:	#1	Pyrex 9 piece "Economy Set" #179 consisting of 8 oz. measuring cup, 9½" pie plate, six 4 oz. custards & handy cup rack	30.00– 35.00
	#2	Pyrex 8 piece "Matched Set" #145 consisting of six 5 oz. custard cups, one 1½ qt. casserole w/pie plate cover in box	25.00– 30.00
Row 5:	#1, 2	Boxes for sets pictured, ea.	4.00– 5.00

"SHIPS," McKee Glass Company, 1930's

Collectors still prefer white lids for their canisters; but if you use these, the clear tops are more convenient for viewing the contents of the dish! Black or red "Ships" are priced similarly. There seems to be more red available than black. All those different "Drippings" containers make you think that there were many grease jar set promotions "back then."

Page 229

Bowl, drippings, 8 oz.	35.00–40.00	Mixing bowl, 9"	18.00–20.00
Bowl, drippings, 16 oz.	35.00–40.00	Mixing bowl, 8"	15.00–18.00
Bowl, drippings, rectangular (4" x 5")	35.00–40.00	Mixing bowl, 7"	12.00–15.00
Bowl, egg beater w/spout, 4½"	40.00–45.00	Mixing bowl, 6"	10.00–12.00
Bowl, beater w/spout, 6½"	30.00–35.00	Pitcher, 2 cup	25.00–30.00
Butter dish	22.00–25.00	Refrigerator dish, 4" x 5"	15.00–18.00
Canister & lid, round, 48 oz., 5"h	35.00–40.00	Refrigerator dish, 5" x 8"	18.00–20.00
Canister & lid, round, 46 oz., 4½"h	35.00–40.00	Shaker, salt or pepper, ea.	9.00–10.00
Canister & lid, round, 24 oz., 3½"h	22.00–25.00	Shaker, flour or sugar, ea.	10.00–12.00
Canister & lid, round, 10 oz., 2½"h	20.00–22.00	Tumbler (or Egg Cup)	15.00–18.00
Mixing bowl set (4)	55.00–65.00		

"SHIPS" and "DUTCH"

These categories are more related than you think. They share the same cabinets at home. Cathy collects both of these, and they are fun to find. You never know what unusual piece will surface. Cathy enjoys them, so I look for them in my travels, hoping not to find a big grouping miles from the car.

Page 230

Row 1:	#1	Jadite, 9¾" bowl, w/windmills	45.00–50.00	*Row 2:*	(Continued)	
	#2, 3	Hocking canister w/Dutch decal, ea.	15.00–20.00		#5-7 Tipp City Dutch shakers, ea.	6.00– 7.00
	#4	Hocking provision jar w/Dutch decal	12.50–15.00	*Row 3:*	#1 Black "Ships" beater bowl, 6½"	30.00–35.00
Row 2:	#1	Windmill "Drippings" (turned wrong)	30.00–35.00		#2 Same, 10 oz. canister	18.00–20.00
	#2	Dutch boy shaker	10.00–12.50		#3 Same, 24 oz.	20.00–22.50
	#3	Dutch boy and girl shakers w/holder	15.00–18.00		#4 Same, 46 oz.	25.00–27.50
	#4	"Churn lady" pr. shakers	15.00–18.00	*Row 4:*	#1 Same, refrigerator dish, 5" x 8"	20.00–22.50
					#2 Same, 4" x 5"	15.00–17.50
					#3 Same, 6" mixing bowl	10.00–12.00

"DUTCH," "DUTCH," and more "DUTCH"

Page 231

Rows 1 & 2: **Hazel Atlas "Skating Dutch"**

	#1	One piece stack set	20.00–22.50	*Row 3:*	#1 Dutch/tulips/windmills, 9" mixing bowl	12.50–15.00
	#2	Three piece stack set	35.00–38.00		#2 Same, 8"	10.00–12.00
	#3	Mixing bowl, 9"	12.50–15.00		#3 Same, 7"	7.50–10.00
	#4	Same, 8"	10.00–12.00		#4 Same, 6"	8.00–10.00
Row 2:	#1	Same, 7"	7.50–10.00	*Row 4:*	#1 Same, 5"	6.00– 8.00
	#2	Same, 6"	8.00–10.00		#2 Fired-on Dutch set w/holder, 3"	25.00–30.00
	#3	Same, 5"	6.00– 8.00			
	#4	Cereal bowl, 5"	6.00– 8.00		#3 Same set, 4"	35.00–40.00
	#5	Salt and pepper pr.	16.00–18.00			

231

LATE ARRIVALS and REPRODUCTIONS

Due to the time lapse between the fourth and fifth editions of this book, several miscellaneous photos were taken at different times. I concluded it was better to have the pieces shown in some form than not at all.

Page 233

Row 1: #1 Hocking pretzel mug, crystal
w/colored stripes 8.00–10.00
#2 Glasbake light yellow
measure cup 25.00–30.00
#3 "Midget" washer 10.00–12.50
#4 Red curtain tie back 12.50–15.00
#5 Federal amber butter tub 25.00–30.00
Row 2: #1 Crystal etched oil and vinegar 20.00–22.50
#2 Blue tie back 12.50–15.00
#3 Percolator part 10.00–12.50
#4 Forest Green cruet 35.00–40.00
#5 Sugar dispenser 12.50– 15.00

Row 3: #1 Duncan "Festive" gravy
boat and ladle 50.00– 55.00
#2 Cake plate and cover 50.00– 55.00
#3 McKee turquoise 6" bowl 35.00– 40.00
#4 Syrup 18.00– 20.00
Row 4: #1 McKee Chalaine blue 7¼", sq. 110.00–125.00
#2 Same 6¼", sq. 90.00–100.00
#3 Straw holder, zippered design 75.00–100.00
#4 Amethyst straw holder 150.00–200.00
#5 Cocktail shaker, cut leaf band 12.50– 15.00

Page 234

Row 1: #1 Glass iron 500.00–600.00
#2 Cambridge cobalt blue
salad set 200.00–250.00
Row 2: #1, 3 Shakers, patriotic "God
Bless America;" "It's Great
to be an American" 15.00– 17.50
#2 Butter dish, Lincoln picture 35.00– 40.00

REPRODUCTIONS – BARNES REAMERS

This picture shows the colors of Barnes (made for Edna Barnes of Uniontown, Ohio) reamers issued as of December 1988. THESE ARE LIMITED EDITION REAMERS. They are collectible in their own right. Some colors are sold out and are selling above the issue price. Three additional colors have been made since 1989. They are pink carnival, milk blue, and opal blue.

Page 235

Rows 1-3: See pages 146 – 147 for original colors. Both the top (inside cone) and the bottom (on the base) are marked with a **B** in a circle. A few of the cobalt blue are marked with an N and not a B, so be aware of that. These will be listed in order they were made. (Some are satinized or frosted).

#1	Cobalt	Row 1, #1	#7	Gold & frosted	Row 2, #4, 5
#2	Rubina	Row 2, #3	#8	Blue Bell & frosted	Row 3, #2, 3
#3	Vaseline & frosted	Row 1, #2, 3	#9	White Milk & painted blue &	Row 3, #4, 5
#4	Black	Row 3, #1		painted pink flowers also	
#5	Apple green & frosted	Row 2, #1, 2	#10	Aqua & frosted (not shown)	
#6	Cranberry Ice & frosted	Row 1, #4, 5	#11	Red (not shown)	

Rows 4-8: Show Barnes reamers which are called 5" and 2½", but really measure 4¾" and 2¼". There is a **B** in a circle on the tab handle of both sizes. Some of these have also been frosted.

Row 1: Heatherbloom, Custard, Green Carnival,
Forest Green
Row 2: Cobalt, Sapphire, Harvest Swirl

Row 3: Cranberry Ice, Gold, Pink Rosemarie
Row 4: Red Glow, Depression Green, Chocolate
Not shown: Milk Blue

REPRODUCTIONS and NEWLY MADE ITEMS

When I wrote the third edition of *Kitchen Glassware*, there were only a few Kitchenware items to report as reproductions. With the demise of Westmoreland Glass Company and the sale of their glass moulds, a whole new world of reproductions appeared. I will approach each item shown on page 237 separately. These are all new! If you wish to purchase any of these, you need to realize that the price for newly made items is determined by seller demand and what the buyer is willing to pay. There is little structured market price especially on the "foreign" made "rip-offs."

Do not be surprised at any color appearing in these items whether it is pictured or not! Know your dealer if you do not know the merchandise! Subscribe to a national trade paper to keep abreast of the latest happenings. (See page 240.)

Row 1: #1-3 – Westmoreland w/oranges and lemons being made by Summit Art Glass in colors of black, "Moonlight" blue, cobalt blue, and "vaseline." Original moulds are being used and only pink, green, and crystal were made originally.

Row 1: #4, 5 – Hazel Atlas 2 cup reamer being made in Far East (likely Taiwan) in green, cobalt blue and pink. THIS IS A MAJOR PROBLEM! Even reamer collectors are having difficulty with this one. The green is easily seen by the horrible color; the pink and blue are fairly true to the originals. They are good copies! The repros all have an oily slick feel and are slightly heavier than the older ones. The repros are wavy and lettering on the sides is slightly different. However, it is impossible to tell you a sure way to tell the old from the new in words so you can feel safe in buying these. I can only emphasize to know who you are dealing with and if the price seems reasonable on an expensive piece, then there might be a good reason. **BUYER BEWARE!**

Row 2: #1-4 – Easley pat. July 10 1888, Sept 10, 1888. Never made in color originally. Original crystal sells $12.00–15.00.

Row 2: #5 – Hazel Atlas cobalt blue three spout, one cup measuring cup made in Taiwan. Spouts are not smoothly made, but it is a good copy.

Row 2: #6 – Hazel Atlas "Kellogg's" embossed cup was made in green and pink in Taiwan. Major difference is on the number 4 in 4 oz. measurement on side. In old, line forming 4 crosses in **middle** of 4 while on new, the perpendicular line crosses ¾ of the way down the 4 in the 4 oz.

Row 3: #1-5 – Gillispie cup w/reamer top made by Summit Art Glass. Cup was never made in color and originally had a measure top instead of reamer top. (See page 117.)

Row 3: #6, 7 – Dry measure w/reamer top made by Summit Art Glass but heretofore, unknown.

Row 4: #1, 2 – Hazel Atlas shakers (salt and pepper) made in Taiwan. Never made in cobalt blue originally. Pink quality varies greatly as do designs. Stippling effect behind embossed salt or pepper is very pronounced on new. New tops are punched in circular pattern.

Row 4: #3 – Fostoria "Colony-like" two spout reamer made originally in white and crystal.

Row 4: #4-7 – Duboe Pat. July 24, 1917, made by Summit and copied without markings in Taiwan. Never made in color originally and sells $40.00–50.00 in crystal.

Row 5: #1-4 – Made by Summit Art Glass from Westmoreland mould. Original colors are shown on page 165 in Rows 3-5. All additional colors are NEW!

Row 6: #1, 3 – Same as dry measures in Row 3: #6, 7 but spout pulled to make measure cup.

Row 6: #2 – Possible Westmoreland cup, footed and spouted and made by Summit in black.

Row 6: #4 – Same as Row 2 without reamer top.

Row 6: #5, 6 – Cobalt blue and black made for Barnes by Imperial in 1981. (Marked IG 81)

LATE ARRIVALS

At the end of our six day photography session last October, we had the following pieces left that didn't make it into other photographs, so here they are! In Row 3 #2 is a pink item that in the past has been sold as a napkin holder. It is part of a Cambridge desk set!

Page 238

Below:	Paramount napkin holder from side and front angles.	400.00–450.00

Page 239

Row 1:	#1	Paden City yellow iced tea	10.00–12.50
	#2	"Handi-Serv Decanter, copyright 1951 General Foods Corp."	5.00–6.00
	#3	Pyrex, 7" bowl	5.00–6.00
	#4	Same, 9" bowl	8.00–10.00
Row 2:	#1	Westmoreland, reamer, 2 part, ice blue	155.00–175.00
	#2	Pyrex, 8" bowl	7.00–8.00
	#3	Percolator top, cobalt blue	18.00–20.00
	#4	Pyrex, 6" bowl	4.00–5.00
	#5	Pyrex, 3½" x 4¾" refrigerator bowl	5.00–6.00
Row 3:	#1	Hazel Atlas pink pint canning jar	20.00–25.00
	#2	"Napkin holder" (piece from Cambridge desk set)	25.00–30.00
	#3	Glasbake meat platter	10.00–12.00
	#4	Butter dish, quarter pound, pink	40.00–50.00
Row 4:	#1	U.S. Glass cake stand or bowl cover	12.50–15.00
	#2	Fry 13" meat platter, pink, "Not Heat Resisting"	70.00—80.00
	#3	Fork, blue handle (Goes with spoon on page 177)	27.50–30.00
	#4,5	Amber salad set w/crystal handles	30.00–35.00
	#6	Imperial amber spoon	27.50–32.50

A publication I recommend:

Books By Gene Florence

Collector's Encyclopedia of Akro Agate Glassware $14.95

Collector's Encyclopedia of Depression Glass.. $19.95

Collectible Glassware from the 40's 50's 60's $19.95

Pocket Guide to Depression Glass $9.95

Collector's Encyclopedia of Occupied Japan I.. $14.95

Collector's Encyclopedia of Occupied Japan II $14.95

Collector's Encyclopedia of Occupied Japan III $14.95

Collector's Encyclopedia of Occupied Japan IV... $14.95

Collector's Encyclopedia of Occupied Japan V.. $14.95

Elegant Glassware of the Depression Era.. $19.95

Very Rare Glassware of the Depression Years $24.95

Very Rare Glassware of the Depression Years Second Series $24.95

Very Rare Glassware of the Depression Years Third Series $24.95

The Standard Baseball Card Price Guide... $9.95